To lengthen thy life,
Lessen thy meals

Benjamin Franklin

(Poor Richard's Almanac, 1733)

Dear Parents

I wrote this book because I care, no other reason. Years ago when I worked with children and the occasional parent, helping them overcome obstacles in their path to a more beneficial life, I sometimes came across an overweight child who appeared happy on the outside, but lonely and sad on the inside. Sure, he/she laughed along with the fat jokes, played the anchoring weight in the tug of war game, and played in the game of life with an ever-present smile. However, I also observed this same child gorging on various foods when he/she thought no one was looking, possibly in an effort to fill the loneliness within. I wanted to reach out and help these kids, but didn't know how at the time. Now I do!

Please know that this is not a diet book, nor a book on nutrition or how to raise 'thin' kids, as we all have different body types. The information and recipes shared in the following pages are offered as a tool to help you raise healthier kids, rather than those burdened by being overweight and at risk of developing weight related diseases.

Raising overweight children does not imply that you are a bad parent, but it does mean that you need to make some better food decisions for your kids. Only you can ensure that your children grow up without excess weight and associated diseases afflicting their bodies.

Sure, change can initially be viewed as difficult, but please have no fear as your love will be your guide and the changes are moderate, tasty and inexpensive. Actually, all you really need to do is pay a bit more attention to what kind and how much food they are eating; while adding some physical activity into their daily routines, ensuring that their muscles develop adequately. The activity portion is easier than you think, as it could be digging a garden, mowing a neighbor's lawn, shoveling snow or joining a YMCA or Recreation Center as a helper. Not all children are athletic, but they do make great helpers. Altering eating habits is easier than you may think too, as it doesn't involve slaving away in the kitchen all day, or counting calories and nutrients. Instead it involves making fewer trips to fast food restaurants, ordering less take-out, serving fewer prepackaged foods, less sugar filled treats and beverages, and eliminating super-sized servings. You see, all you really need to do is love your kids a little bit more, while feeding them a little bit less!

The tasty path that follows is easy and deliciously full-flavored, so hop onto the trails toward happier and healthier children and enjoy the journey.

Randi/The Muffin Lady

This cookbook offers guidance, support and recipes for helping parents and caregivers avoid raising severely overweight and obese kids with ease and memorable flavors.

✧

Several of the recipes within these pages can also be found formatted for use in higher elevations in Randi's High Altitude Cookbooks:

Baking at High Altitude, ISBN: 978009745009-1-X
Sharing Mountain Recipes, ISBN: 978009745009-2-9

✧

This book is published by:
The Muffin Lady Incorporated
1532 Yankee Creek Road
Evergreen, Colorado 80439 USA

Copyright May, 2010: The Muffin Lady Incorporated, Randi L. Levin
Publication Date: 2010

For any questions concerning the preparation of any of the recipes or information in the following, please e-mail The Muffin Lady at: themuffinlady@yahoo.com

The characters on the cover and within the pages of this book are fictitious. Any similarity to real people is only coincidental and not intended to offend by the author.

ISBN# 978-0-9745008-3-6

Mixed Sources
Product group from well-managed
forests and other controlled sources
www.fsc.org Cert no. SW-COC-002283
© 1996 Forest Stewardship Council
FSC

Printed on recycled paper, in the United States
by ImagiCom Media Graphics, Inc.

$ 12.99

Acknowledgements

To my mom, grandmothers and aunts, although most of you have gone to a better place, I thank you with all my heart for the lessons taught, memories shared and the endless hours spent preparing daily meals, including altering a few for a fussy eater.

How can I ever thank all the teachers, professors and doctors who took the time to teach a curious mind? The patience you illustrated with my endless questions, persistent interruptions and hungry will to learn and seek understanding, are priceless treasures that I hold close to my heart, deep in my gut, and clearly in my mind.

Lots of bear hugs to **Stuart Smoller**, my fine editor, who has an amazing skill for zooming in on grammatical errors, typos and misalignments. Your skills shine my friend, and for such I am eternally grateful.

Corey Hiseler, my copyeditor, indexer, and occasional conscience, how can I ever begin to thank you for all the questions asked, redirection of words, focus on coherence, sampling of my recipes and simply being there in times of need? Although miles away, you held my hand through these pages as only a friend can! Thus, hugs and kisses for your time, skills, patience, caramel chocolates and most of all your friendship.

Betsy Jueschke, I am eternally grateful to you for calling me that one afternoon many moons ago and sharing Julie, your Creative Designer with me. I wish you success, happiness and tables filled with many joys!

Julie Eardley, wow how did I ever get so lucky to have you as my Creative Designer! What you have so skillfully and beautifully done with my manuscript is short of a miracle.

Robert A. "Zeek" Kropf, my wonderful Illustrator, you are a God-send. Your skills for interpreting my words into images are that of a true artist and for that I am immensely grateful to have you on my team!

These pages are dedicated to

the kids of the world.

May life's path

fill you with

Adventures,

Happiness,

Energy

Good Health

and the

Flavors of Fresh

Homemade Love!

Table of Contents

Introduction

The first and most important step that you can take on the path toward avoiding raising severely overweight and obese kids is to acknowledge that your child is overweight. Sometimes, those 'rose colored glasses' are easier to put on, than admit that something might be wrong with your child. Yes, the social stigmas related to raising an overweight child can be overwhelming at best; thus many parents try to deny or avoid this issue in an effort to protect themselves and their children from other's abuses. Parents may tell themselves and others that their child looks to be about the right weight, that they're only a little chubby, but not fat; or that they're even underweight when compared to everyone else in the family. But these are only excuses you make to yourself and those around you. Just because your child is overweight does not imply that you are a bad parent; or that your child is stupid and lazy, as others may say!

However, the earlier that you acknowledge that you child has a weight issue, the easier the path will be toward protecting them from developing weight related stigmas and illnesses. It is important to recognize that surveys and research at The Nemours Foundation have found that about one third of children in the United States alone, are severely overweight or obese. Additionally, research at the Center for Disease Control and Prevention (CDC) confirms that, "*10% of babies and toddlers are precariously heavy.*" And when other recent studies found that "*1 in 5 American 4-year-olds is obese*" particularly among minorities, (National Center for Education Statistics, 2007), and that about "*43% of parents deny that their 6-11 year old are overweight*" (Associated Press, 2007) then obviously the time has arrived for you to acknowledge that your child has a weight issue and to begin making some moderate changes in eating and behavioral habits simply for the sake of your child's health and overall well-being.

Sure, those cute, chubby cheeks are precious and roly-poly babies are adorable, but as a child grows they begin to move around more, the rolls of baby fat should naturally develop into some muscle, not more rolls. Thus if you notice that as your toddler grows, that they are still carrying around excess rolls of flab, then instead of denying it or writing it off as something that they'll grow out of, do something about it. This applies to school age kids too; for when pre-teens and teens have a weight problem, some parents excuse excessive weight gains as something that they will grow out of as they mature. For girls, the excuse is that once they have their period, the baby fat will dissolve. Or for the boys, once they get taller their weight will balance out. Of course this is true for many, but for some it just doesn't happen. Actually, while researching the statistics on Childhood Obesity, I found several studies, revealing that when a child is severely overweight or obese between ages 10-13, then they are 65%-80% more likely to be obese adults.

Accompanying these studies, it has been shown that when a child is born into a family in which members are overweight and/or obese, the risk of raising overweight, potentially obese children, rises significantly. Yes, heredity does play a role in what we are going to look like as an adult, but it's not a justified excuse for raising overweight, potentially ill and obese children. Therefore, when family members have a tendency to be overweight, I ask that you make a distinction between what I refer to as "*big*" and "*large*" body types. Many people have big, beautiful bodies. That is, their bones and body frame might be big and thick, but still relatively firm. A large body on the other hand, is one that may have big bones and body frame, but their body is primarily soft and flabby. With this distinction stated, please do not use the excuse that "everyone in our family is large" to rationalize your child's excessive weight. Inheriting a big body frame is not an excuse for overeating, not exercising, and being too large, soft, and flabby.

How can you recognize when your child begins to gain too much excess weight? You look at their body, and see if they have a few extra rolls that are just too soft when compared to other children of the same age. You look to see if their muscles are growing adequately or if your child's belly, arms and legs are lumpy and jiggle. You notice if their belly begins to flow over their belt buckle, bulge atop their pants, or roundly protrude under their tee shirt, and if they skip meals in favor of sweet and/or salty alternatives?

Taking off those 'rose colored glasses' is the first step toward avoiding raising obese children. But once you take those shades off, what can you do, especially when the budget is strained and you are at work all day? Should you put them on a diet and eliminate all sweets and snacks from your home? No! Diets only work temporarily and can cause an obsession with or avoidance to food. Also, diets can possibly cause the hoarding of unhealthy choices, when opportunities arise. Besides, it is always best to make dietary adjustments for your whole family, not just one member. So what can do to help your kids? You take the easiest path possible, and illustrate your love for them a little more, by feeding everyone in your family less fat, salt and sugar laced previously prepared and prepackaged foods in favor of easily prepared, homemade goodness. In addition, you begin to provide fun and motivating options that promote and increase their involvement in physical activities. Difficult to ponder, maybe, but it's actually very easy to accomplish with dedication, consistency and heart.

THE SPICE RACK

The Spice Rack

A long time ago, a friend attempted to cook dinner one night. He knew that I baked and cooked for others all day long, and wanted to surprise me with a homemade offering of his love. Sadly, he didn't know which spices and herbs to use. Needless to say, his efforts ended up in the dog's bowl; and I whipped up a couple tuna sandwiches for dinner. If only he had asked which herbs or spices blend best with a food, his expensive endeavor could have been avoided; but he was too embarrassed to ask.

Many people feel embarrassed to question which spices and herbs mingle best with specific foods, so their culinary efforts end up bland and boring, or severely over-seasoned and unpalatable. However, as the old-line states, "You'll never know until you ask." Therefore, with this stated, know that just a pinch of the right spice, or a tablespoon of a fresh chopped herb, can really turn a plain, everyday dish into one offering magnificent flavor that will be eagerly gobbled and requested again and again.

For the convenience of those not very experienced in the kitchen, as well as to prevent any confusion as to what spice or herb blends best when accentuating the flavor of homemade food, please examine the following lists of natural spices and herbs to use when enhancing the flavor of your home cooked endeavors. In the condiment section, you will find the recommended average serving sizes to help you make moderate changes in your eating habits.

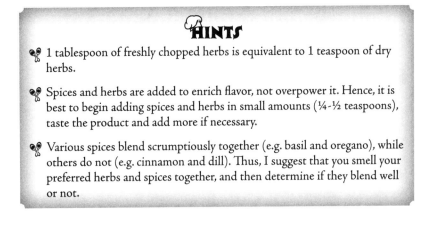

HINTS

- 1 tablespoon of freshly chopped herbs is equivalent to 1 teaspoon of dry herbs.

- Spices and herbs are added to enrich flavor, not overpower it. Hence, it is best to begin adding spices and herbs in small amounts (¼-½ teaspoons), taste the product and add more if necessary.

- Various spices blend scrumptiously together (e.g. basil and oregano), while others do not (e.g. cinnamon and dill). Thus, I suggest that you smell your preferred herbs and spices together, and then determine if they blend well or not.

Herbs and Spices

ALLSPICE: A sweet spice that blends the essences of cinnamon, cloves and nutmeg together, with a hint of pepper. Primarily used in baked goods such as pies, cakes, and muffins. Just a dash can also enhance food such as chicken dishes, meats, sauces and stuffing.

ANISE: A strong, licorice-flavored spice often found in sweets and pastries.

BASIL: Commonly used in pasta based sauces (e.g. tomato-based, pesto, alfredo) and various soups. The wonderfully warm, sweet flavor also pairs deliciously with roasts, stews, vegetables, dressings, and omelets made with fresh vegetables.

BAY LEAF: A splendid savory leaf, with a hint of sweetness, is commonly added to soups, stews, meats and veggie dishes. (Cook, roast or simmer in the food, but remember to remove before serving.)

BOUQUET GARNI: A bundle of fresh herbs often combined with a vegetable (celery stalk with leaves attached) that is commonly tied with a string or twisty, a cheesecloth bag or placed in an old, clean nylon stocking. Used to flavor soups, stocks and various stews, the "bouquet" is simmered with required recipe ingredients, but removed and discarded before serving.

CAPERS: Commonly, used to elegantly spice fish, especially salmon. Capers are salty, strong and pungent in flavor. When added to salads, sauces or on top of pizza or pastas, the essence is uniquely spicy. Also they pair exceptionally well when pickling various vegetables or meats.

CARAWAY: This splendid seed offers a sweet, but tangy flavor, and is commonly used in Rye breads, cakes, soups, cheeses, and sauerkraut.

CARDAMON: Known to elicit a fragrantly sweet, eucalyptus, slightly lemony flavor, this lovely spice is commonly used in sweet breads, fruit salad dressings, cookies, cakes, and as a pickling spice.

CAYENNE PEPPER: A spicy hot, ground spice primarily used to increase the heat offered in such comforting delights as chilies and stews. Often used interchangeably with Tabasco® or a hot sauce.

CELERY SEED: Similar in flavor to fresh celery, this seed can commonly be found ground or in tiny whole seeds. Used as a delicious spice to accentuate the flavor of diverse foods ranging from soups and stews to salads and dips. Although you can find a similar variety commonly called celery salt, ground celery seed has a fresher, more comforting flavor.

CHERVIL: Often referred to as "gourmet parsley" and a favorite of French chefs, chervil offers a hint of anise in flavor and is most commonly used to season elaborate dishes made of poultry and seafood, as well as soups, eggs, and/or vegetables.

CHIVES: Offering a sweet, mild onion flavor, chives are frequently added to soups, potatoes, fish, and various dips. Besides its savory culinary virtues, I have found that when planted in the garden, this herb's fragrance helps keep the critters away from devouring my flowers.

CILANTRO: Also called fresh coriander and commonly referred to as Chinese parsley, has a flavor resembling a mix of parsley and citrus. Most commonly used in Mexican dishes such as chilies, dips and salsas, but flavors just as nicely in stir-fried veggies and salads.

CINNAMON: This favorite spice has a sweet aroma and the flavor offered is mouthwatering. This spice is most commonly used in baked goods and puddings, although it pairs scrumptiously with cereals, stews, poultry and some sauces. Additionally, one of the best features of this wonderful spice is that it also functions as a natural sweetener, and research is currently being conducted into its possible role in preventing Type 2 Diabetes.

CLOVES: This rich, sweetly pungent spice originated in East Africa, is used ground in baked goods and whole when seasoning poultry, baked hams, and meats and/or stews.

CORIANDER: Being the seed of the cilantro plant, coriander offers a uniquely mild flavor similar to a soft blending of sage and lemon; and used most commonly when preparing and cooking spicy sausages and meats.

CUMIN: Known to draw out the natural sweetness of various foods such as tomatoes, chili peppers and salsas; this nutty flavored spice is most commonly found as a seasoning in Indian, Mexican, Cuban and Middle Eastern foods.

CURRY POWDER: A sweet, tasty blend of various spices (turmeric, cumin, coriander, cinnamon, cloves and chili pepper powder), most commonly found in Oriental and Indian dishes. Some chefs will even add this blend of spices to fruits when seeking a uniquely pleasing flavor.

DILL: In the recipes that follow, you will notice that I add dill to many of my recipes for soups, salads and dressings simply for its refreshing, but distinctive flavor. I find that just a pinch of its fresh, aromatic essence can literally change a plain old everyday food into one of spectacular delight.

FENNEL SEEDS: The mild, though sweetly hot anise flavor offered is crisp and fresh, especially when added to pork, fish, and several Italian favorites such as sausages and meatballs. These seeds can also be used to enhance the flavor in cereals, yeast and sweet breads.

FIVE SPICE CHINESE POWDER: Ingredients include anise, cinnamon, star anise, cloves, and ginger. Commonly found in Chinese foods, this fragrant combination of spices enhances the flavors of meats, poultry and fish, although it is especially good when added to stir-fry or when combined with soy or teriyaki sauce.

GARLIC: Garlic is one of the most favored spices used to season food today. Personally, I believe you can never add enough garlic, especially to tomato-based sauces and stews. Although not often used for baked goods (except some breads), garlic can be used to enhance the flavor of most foods, especially meats, poultry, fish and vegetables. For best flavor, use fresh garlic cloves or minced garlic, rather than the powdered varieties.

GINGER: Sweetly warm and woody, ginger offers a clean, spicy flavor. Commonly used in sodas, teas, oriental dishes and baked goods, ginger can be found fresh, crystallized or candied, ground or as a syrup. Ginger has been found to help eliminate gas, diarrhea, and nausea. Plus it has been said to help to temper a runny nose as well as a sore throat.

HORSERADISH: Most commonly found mixed with cream and called Horseradish Sauce, this spicy and pungent herb is often used on beef roasts, sausages, and with fish. Many currently enjoy wasabi (on peas and in sauces), which is simply a variety of horseradish previously mixed with mustard and food dye.

JUNIPER BERRIES: With a woody, pine essence; juniper berries are usually found in dishes made from wild game and lamb.

LEMON PEPPER: Combining the lovely scent of lemon zest with the ground pepper, acts as a tenderizer for meats while accentuating the flavor of various poultry, fish, seafood and pasta dishes. Just a little sprinkle can really jazz up those everyday dishes into one that may be requested for years to come.

LOVE: Adding extra spoonfuls of this universally, miraculous spice is highly recommended for sprinkling on all homemade food. Just a dash can increase the flavor of all good deeds. You see, love, added to everything, always makes it a little bit better!

MACE: Comes from the lacy outer shell of nutmeg, but more pungent in flavor. It is a fragrant spice used in a vast variety of foods including soups, cream sauces, lamb, chicken, stews, cheeses, stuffing, sausages, steamed puddings, ketchup, and a few baked goods.

MARJORAM: Delicately sweet, with just a hint of bitterness in flavor this pungent, aromatic herb is used dried or fresh to season lamb, poultry, seafood, and also as a seasoning for blended vegetables.

MINT: Filled with the scent of wide-open spaces, mint is most commonly found in flavors of spearmint and peppermint. This refreshing, sweet herb can be used fresh or dry to flavor lamb, poultry, vegetables, and fruits. Chocolate mint leaves can be dried and crushed and then easily added to baked goods when seeking a slight change in flavor, such as sugar or chocolate cookies. Mint is also very easy to grow in a small garden or even on a sunny windowsill.

MUSTARD: Mustard, a naturally hot and pungent spice is available in three forms: whole seeds, dried powder and prepared with a liquid to be easily spread. Although the uses for mustard are plentiful, most likely you will find it hidden in non-leafy salads (i.e. potato salad), dressings, and sauces.

NUTMEG: A tad sweeter than its lacy outer coating mace, nutmeg is a wonderful spice offering a fragrantly sweet, woodsy flavor. It is quite versatile, for just a pinch of nutmeg can magically turn a variety of soups, sauces, potatoes, ciders or even eggs into a dish fit for royalty. This wonderful spice is often used in baked goods, and pairs well with cinnamon in cakes, cookies and muffins. In addition, it will enrich the flavor of peaches, when they are added to poultry dishes or various baked treats.

OREGANO: A Mediterranean herb, offering flavor and fragrance, it can often be found in vegetable-based sauces and salads. Use fresh or dried in all types of savory dishes, especially those of Italian or Spanish origin.

PAPRIKA: Often used as a garnish or to alter the color of sauces (for example hollandaise sauce) this flavorful food ranges from mildly sweet to hot in flavor, can be sprinkled on a diverse variety of foods, including casseroles, baked potatoes, appetizers, poultry, veal, and salad dressings. Whereby Hungarian Paprika offers the most flavor, American brands are usually bland in comparison.

PARSLEY: Commonly used herb, filled with a fresh but light essence, is often found fresh or dry in soups and salads or as a garnish for poultry or seafood dishes. Available in two varieties: the curly leaf type and the flat leaf, or Italian type. Best when used fresh but can be used dry.

PEPPER: A common household spice, filled with immune building antioxidants, offers a pinch of heat with a hint of sweetness in flavor. Many often season beef with lots of pepper, but a sprinkling or two on salads, potatoes and veggies is just as common. Often the amount of pepper added to foods is a matter of personal taste, so allow individuals to add their own once the foods are cooked and the plates are set upon the table, unless indicated otherwise.

POPPY SEED: These wonderfully nutty and sweetly flavored tiny black seeds are commonly used to enhance fruit and veggie salad dressings, as well as a variety of baked treats such as muffins, cakes, strudels and breads.

PUMPKIN PIE SPICE: A blend of cinnamon, ginger, allspice, nutmeg, and cloves in equal proportions. This fragrant spice is commonly used in baked or sweet tasting foods such as pumpkin pie, gingerbread, cookies, fruits, squash, sweet potatoes, applesauce and a few other apple dishes.

ROSEMARY: A piney flavor perennial related to the mint, is often used to enrich the flavor of poultry and sautéed meat dishes and soups, while also adding a nice fresh flavor to fruits, salads, dressings and poultry stuffing.

SAFFRON: Known to be the world's most expensive spice, this orange-yellowish, bitter aromatic spice is often used to add a colorful presence in some foods that would otherwise appear dull in color. Commonly found in risotto (Italian rice), this spice can also be added to soups, poultry dishes, and fancy European breads.

SAGE: Slightly bitter, but warm to taste, this herb is used either fresh or dried. It pairs particularly well with fresh or cured pork, lamb, veal, poultry, beans, or vegetables.

SALT: Although there are various types of salt available in today's markets, please know that sea salt is the most natural, flavorful, and healthful of all. Salt enriches the flavors of foods and helps yeast products to rise properly. However, adding too much salt to food can be detrimental to health. Additionally, salt helps preserve some canned, processed, and frozen foods; thus, when choosing these foods, choose those with lower sodium listing on the label. Many baked recipes require a minimal addition of salt, but you will notice that I do not add any to my baked recipes because I find it an unnecessary ingredient, unless baking yeast-based products or biscuits.

SAVORY: The wonderfully piney scent and peppery flavored herb helps to adds pizzazz to the flavor of food whether used alone or in combination with other herbs (such as rosemary and thyme). Use for seasoning meat, fish or poultry, as well as in egg dishes, sauces, soups, stews, beans, cabbage, and various vegetable juices.

SESAME SEEDS: Mildly sweet, nutty flavored seeds are often used in appetizers, breads, cookies, poultry, and vegetables.

TARRAGON: A sweet, fragrant herb, usually added to poultry and seafood, although it enhances the flavors of some soups, sauces, salads, and vegetables as well.

THYME: A fragrant, slightly minty small leaf herb is popular fresh or dried as a seasoning for poultry, seafood, or vegetables.

TURMERIC: Turmeric is the root of a plant belonging to the ginger family and has a yellowish tone to it. Commonly said to have a bitter flavor, but an exotically combination of orange and ginger in fragrance, this lovely herb is most commonly found in various types of mustard and in many Indian and Mediterranean foods. In fact turmeric is what gives curry powder its yellowish color.

ZEST: Zest is the grated peel of citrus fruits, often added for flavoring to some baked goods as well as fish and seafood dishes. Occasionally, the zest of a fruit is added to poultry dishes garnished and flavored with fresh fruit (e.g. lemon chicken).

Common Commercial Sauces

SOY SAUCE: An Asian seasoning and condiment made from soybeans, wheat or other grain, salt and water. Use this rich condiment sparingly to enrich the flavor of diverse dishes ranging from poultry and seafood to meat, veggies, and stir-fry. Hint: Chinese brands tend to be saltier than Japanese brands.

TABASCO®: A hot, liquid peppery sauce used to accentuate the flavor of numerous dishes such as eggs, stews, chilies, sauces, meats, poultry, and fish. Add sparingly, as only a few drops are necessary.

TARTAR SAUCE: This tangy and spicy sauce is commonly served as a dip to accentuate the flavor of fish and seafood.

TERIYAKI SAUCE: Primarily used as a marinade for fish, seafood, poultry, and meat, as well as a basting sauce for grilling and stir-fry.

WORCESTERSHIRE SAUCE: Intensely flavorful, this savory sauce is a blend of many ingredients, including molasses, soy sauce, garlic, onion, and anchovies. Popular as a marinade ingredient or as a table sauce for foods, especially red meats, this wonderful sauce is usually sprinkled onto beef or wild game prior to cooking.

✧

Food Condiments

- ✧ The following items should be used sparingly, *not excessively*. These condiments are used to enhance and moisten some food, rather than overwhelm and hide the flavors of the main ingredients.

- ✧ Use of too much of the following condiments can induce unwanted weight gain, so use them sparingly rather than to saturate the final product.

BBQ SAUCE: Provides a sweet tangy flavor to meats, poultry and fish, but should be used sparingly or it may hide the actual flavor of the food that it is meant to enhance. 1-2 tablespoons is a sufficient amount, more is too much.

BUTTER, MARGARINE AND SPREADS: These wonderful condiments are included in the preparation of many foods. However, when using them as an accessory, such as to enhance the flavor of breads or vegetables, they should be applied sparingly rather than in globs. 1-3 teaspoons per serving is usually an adequate amount when enhancing the flavor of food.

CREAM CHEESE: As soft as a pillow, but mighty in flavor, cream cheese is found in many different foods ranging from baked treats to sauces, fillings and dips. Because it is as high in calories as it is in flavor, it should be used as one would use butter—sparingly rather than in globs.

JAMS, JELLIES, AND PRESERVES: Primarily made from fruits, sugars and gelatin, these delicious condiments can be used as spreads for breads, as additions to various baked goods, and as flavor enhancers for poultry, pork and beef. They provide a fabulous taste, but should be used sparingly, rather than in spoonfuls, as most varieties are high in calories. 100% fruit preserves are recommended for flavor and nourishment, as chunks of real fruit are provided, whereas jellies and some jams are primarily made from sugar, gelatin, artificial flavoring and a minimum of fruit.

KETCHUP: I have watched many a child drowning foods with an excess of this favored condiment, resulting in hiding the flavor of food rather than enhancing its flavor. Because ketchup is made from numerous ingredients, including different sugars, limiting its use decreases the amount of sugar ingested.

MAPLE SYRUP: Maple syrup is a favorite flavor enhancer for various breakfast foods baked treats and poultry. Filled with immunity building minerals such as zinc, maple syrup is much better for the body than granulated sugar and the artificial maple flavored varieties. A recommended serving is approximately 2 tablespoons, not ¼ cup or more. To enhance the maple flavor in chosen foods, add ½ teaspoon pure maple extract to the batter, hence eliminating any desire to saturate the final product with too much syrup.

MAYONNAISE: One of the most abused condiments used today! Many add too much when preparing food such as sandwiches and salads. Mayonnaise can pack on extra pounds when used excessively. Thus, just decreasing the amount you use by a tablespoon or two for sandwiches, and more when preparing salads (such as tuna salad), can make a huge difference when preventing unwanted weight gain. Also, yogurt can be used in place of or combined with mayonnaise for a fulfilling, but much less fattening offering.

SALAD DRESSINGS: Oil or creamy based, these delicious condiments enrich many different foods, most commonly those made from vegetables and fruits.

Because most commercial varieties are high in calories, fat, and sodium (salt), I recommend that you use these sparingly and/or make your own, adding your own herbs and spices to taste. Average serving size is approximately 2 tablespoons, not ¼ cup or more per salad.

SOUR CREAM: This wonderful condiment is so versatile that it can be used in baked goods, salads and sauces as well as to mingle the flavors of numerous foods. Offering a cool, soothing complement, its use should be limited to "a little dab will do you," such as on baked potatoes or chili. Unfortunately, sour cream is very fattening. One of the best ways to cut much of the fat from sour cream is to add a large scoop of plain yogurt to it and thoroughly mix it in before serving. Plain yogurt can also be substituted for sour cream in most foods, including baked goods and dips. These minor changes provide an excellent way to help you make better food decisions for your kids without sacrificing flavor.

YOGURT: A naturally creamy offering of comfort, yogurt helps build strong bones and teeth, while keeping our body's blood flowing smoothly through our veins. Plain Yogurt is one of those foods that you honestly cannot get enough of. When trying to lose weight or prevent unwanted weight gains, yogurt is a super food that cannot be denied. It can be used as a substitute for cream cheese, buttermilk (depending on recipe), heavy cream, sweet cream, and most importantly mayonnaise and sour cream.

The Power of Homemade Love

❦

For many, just the thought of having to actually cook more food and prepare snacks on a regular basis may be a tad daunting. Yet, keep in mind that the act of cooking good, homemade food offers the magic of a blessing. It keeps your loved ones close, fills their hearts with warmth, their bodies with energy, and their memories with smiles! You see, the power of well-prepared homemade food is astounding! Homemade food helps to bring families together at the table, while developing memories and tastes that last a lifetime. And it really doesn't take much time to toss a flavorful meal or healthy snack together to keep your family happy, healthy and satisfied. It does however, take a pinch of effort, but isn't your family worth it?

Because it does take time to prepare certain foods, a fun project to get into the habit of is cooking a few foods (e.g. a pot of soup, while a meatloaf cooks in the oven) for the week ahead during the weekends and refrigerating or freezing them for use later in the week. The kids can help in the kitchen too, as the lessons learned will help prepare them for the years ahead. It is in the comforting essence of your home kitchen, whether large or small, where your children will develop memories of fragrant, good flavors, skills to last a lifetime, and values to carry with them into the years to come. There are many reasons why we all have a tendency to hang out in the warming glow of a home kitchen and food is not the only one. Timeless treasures get shared in the kitchen, such as that first kiss between your mom and dad, or how your Uncle bullied everyone as a kid until he didn't have any friends left. Or imagine your children learning about fractions while measuring ingredients, or just how to make a great pot of soup when there is no recipe. Your kitchen's walls simmer with an aroma of knowledge and flavor. Hence, you will not just be cooking, you will be spending quality time with your children, teaching them lessons to be carried on and shared for generations to come. Cooking for your family should not be viewed as stressful, but as a priceless opportunity to share precious moments with your children, while helping them develop values and fond memories to be cherished and carried in the heart throughout their years ahead.

❦

The Wonderful World of Chicken Soup

There is no canned variety of soup that is comparable to homemade. Just think of how many luscious recipes you can make from just a large pot of chicken soup? This one fragrant pot of love can produce meals for weeks to come. You can serve the soup as is, make chicken pot pie from frozen leftovers later in the month, make chicken sandwiches or dinners in a jiffy, chicken salad to die for, and even use some of the reserved stock for various stuffing's or sauces. Just the act of allowing a variety of fresh ingredients to slowly simmer for hours spreads a most enticing, mouth-watering fragrance throughout your home. For your convenience, I have listed a couple of incredibly tasty recipes to prepare from the leftovers after this recipe. And, if you do not have a 2-3 gallon stockpot, I suggest that you get one, as the their value is endless.

✧

2-3 gallon pot, with a lid

1 tablespoon chicken soup (bouillon) crystals

5-6 pounds chicken previously cut into pieces

1 large onion, peeled with first layer removed

1 bunch fresh parsley (2-3 ounces)

1 bunch fresh dill (3-4 ounces)

1 rounded teaspoon minced garlic

1 bunch celery, washed, with 3-4 stalks removed and chopped into 2-inch pieces

4-5 carrots, washed and chopped into 3-inch lengths

1⅓ cup lima beans (optional)

1 plus tablespoon kosher salt (more may be added later if needed)

Pepper to taste

1. Thoroughly wash the chicken, and then cut off any excess pieces of fat. Once thoroughly washed, place the chicken pieces into the pot and cover them completely with water. Bring the water to a boil and skim all the scum from the top with a large spoon.

2. Add 1-2 more cups of water.

3. To make a bouquet garni, tie the parsley, dill and remaining celery with a small string or place these ingredients into the toe of an old nylon stocking; securing it tightly at the top of the celery with string or twist-tie. (Cut off and discard any excess nylon.)

4. Place the bouquet garni into the pot of boiling water, and then add all of the remaining ingredients to the pot. Bring the water back to a boil, skim the scum from the top again, and add 1 more cup of warm water. Lower the heat to a very slow simmer. Keep the soup pot covered with a lid.

5. Allow the soup to simmer for 6-8 hours, tasting after about 3-4 hours and then adding more seasonings if you like. This soup is finished cooking when the chicken is tender and begins to pull away from the bones.

6. Before removing anything from the pot, remove any excess fat from the top of the soup, by placing two paper towels on top of the broth, let the towels sit for a few seconds and discard. Then remove the bouquet garni from the soup.

7. Using a colander or large sieve and slotted spoon, remove all ingredients from the broth, allowing them to strain over the pot, and then place them onto a large plate. Discard all of the bones and skin pieces. You may want to separate the vegetables, stock, and chicken into three separate bowls, to ensure that all bones have been removed.

8. At this point you can either break part of the chicken into small pieces and then return them and the veggies to the soup pot, or keep them separate when serving the chicken and veggies as the main course. (Or you can return some of the smaller pieces of chicken and veggies back to the pot and keep the majority separate, the choice is yours to make.)

9. Serve the soup in individual bowls with previously prepared thin egg noodles, alphabet noodles or rice. Keep in mind that there are some children who only like broth with noodles, and prefer that the chicken be served separately on a plate.

HINTS

- If freezing the broth, I suggest freezing half of the broth in a large container and then divide the remaining broth between smaller, separate containers to be used in future recipes and culinary creations.

- Instead of using paper towels to remove the excess fat, you can allow the soup to cool, and then remove the fat after as it solidifies.

- Do not store or freeze the soup with noodles in it, as the noodles will become mushy and unpalatable.

Chicken Pot Pie

Easy, pleasing, and comforting! The best part is that this divine recipe only takes minutes to prepare, especially with leftovers from the soup. Then all you need to do is add a few more veggies, cover it with a pie crust and toss it in the oven for a short period of time (enough to help the kids with their homework), and you have a healthy, hearty homemade meal.

✧

Preheat oven to 375° Fahrenheit   **Serves 6-8**

One 9-inch homemade or one prepackaged pie shell

6 tablespoons unsalted butter

6 tablespoons flour

2-2½ cups homemade chicken broth

¼ teaspoon each, dill, thyme, rosemary, and nutmeg or cloves

½ teaspoon minced garlic

4 cups chopped previously cooked and skinned chicken (i.e. soup chicken)

2 tablespoons butter or margarine

2 carrots, washed and sliced into ¼ inch pieces

2 celery stalks, washed and diced

1 small onion, diced

1 cup fresh or frozen peas, thawed and drained

½ cup corn kernels, fresh or frozen, thawed and drained

¾ cup chopped fresh broccoli (optional)

⅓ cup raisins (optional)

Sea salt and pepper to taste

HINT

🥄 Due to the fact that pie crusts are loaded with calories and fat, I do not use a bottom crust when preparing pot pies, as I find it unnecessary.

1. Thoroughly grease a deep-dish pie pan with pan spray, butter, or margarine and set aside.

2. Make a roux by melting the butter in a large saucepan and stirring in the flour. Cook and stir this mixture for 2-3 minutes over medium heat or until it turns pasty and a light brown color. Gradually add the broth and spices, and then stir the roux constantly until thickened and smooth about 6-7 minutes.

3. Lower the heat to low and thoroughly stir all remaining ingredients into the saucepan. Allow all the ingredients to simmer for a few minutes.

4. Pour the mixture of ingredients into the prepared pie pan. Cover the ingredients thoroughly with the pie shell, fold the edge over and onto itself and flute the edges by pinching the dough together every half inch or so.

5. Bake the pot pie for 30-40 minutes or until the crust is golden brown.

6. Allow the pie to cool and set for 5 minutes before serving.

HINTS

- You can use 1-pound skinless, boneless chicken or turkey breasts, washed, fat removed and cut into pieces and then boiled or grilled until pierced and juices run clear.

- Previously cooked beef (i.e. pot roast beef) or pork can be used in place of chicken

Chicken Salad to Die For

Years ago when I had a small bakery and deli, this was one of my most popular recipes. Luscious, comforting and filled with a marvelous flavor that emanates the goodness of homemade, guarantees that this recipe will become a household favorite upon first bite.

4-4½ cups chopped and shredded previously cooked chicken or turkey

2 tablespoons chicken broth

1 cup celery, diced

1 cup red onions, diced

1½ cups plus red grapes, sliced in half

⅓ cup mayonnaise

2 tablespoons plain yogurt

1-2 teaspoons minced garlic

1 teaspoon celery seed

1¼ teaspoons dill

Sea salt and pepper to taste

½ cup chopped pecans, walnuts or almonds (optional)

HINTS

Beware of adding more mayonnaise than the suggested amount. Excess mayonnaise can contribute to excess weight gain, and the amount suggested is more than adequate for this recipe, especially when pre-mixed with yogurt. Remember. An average serving size of mayonnaise is only 2 tablespoons per day, not per meal.

Although this recipe works great as a sandwich or wrap, due to the fact that most kids get much more bread than necessary, why not try serving this divine delight on top of shredded lettuce, cucumber slices, or smear about 2 rounded tablespoons onto the wide end of a large piece of lettuce and then roll it up as you would a wrap. Two lettuce rolls are an appropriate serving for little ones, three for preteens and four for older children.

1. Boil the chicken or turkey thoroughly in a large pot of water, unless using leftovers. Once the chicken has thoroughly boiled, drain out all juice, but 2 tablespoons. Pour the reserved juice and chicken into a large bowl and chop the chicken into 1-inch chunks, shredding the largest of these by simply rubbing them apart between your fingers. (This shredding procedure is important, for it assists in making this salad creamier, while still keeping some chunks in the final product.)

2. Add and mix all remaining ingredients, except the nuts, together with the chicken.

3. Refrigerate the salad for at least 2 hours allowing the flavors to blend. If adding nuts, sprinkle them on top of this salad prior to serving.

Homemade Chunky Tomato Sauce

This wonderful recipe is superb in flavor and one that I can promise will become a family favorite. The best part about this recipe is that you can alter it to fit your family's tastes. If you're vegetarian, then don't add the meat; if your children do not like peppers, then don't add them. If your family enjoys hot, spicy foods, use hot Italian sausage; or you can use ground turkey or turkey Italian sausages. Whichever ingredients you choose, know that just the scent of goodness that flows out your door, can get the kids off the corner or computer and to the dinner table, before you even announce that dinner is ready.

✧

Makes approximately 1.5 gallons

¼-⅓ cup virgin olive oil

1 plus pound Italian sausage, cut into 1-2 inch chunks (mild or hot sausage, depending on how spicy your family prefers their food)

1 plus pound ground beef

1 medium onion, diced

5-7 garlic cloves, diced

Two 28-ounce cans tomato sauce

18-ounces tomato paste

½ cup red wine (or more)

½-⅔ cup minced fresh spinach

½ green pepper, seeded and finely diced

1½ teaspoons oregano

1 teaspoon sweet basil

Scant ½ teaspoon marjoram

Scant ½ teaspoon thyme

Scant ½ teaspoon sage

¼ cup grated Parmesan and/or Romano cheese

1-2 tablespoons honey or 1-2 teaspoons baking soda

2 medium zucchinis, cut into ¼-inch slices

1. Cut one of the garlic cloves in half and then rub it along the sides and bottom of a 2-gallon or larger stockpot. Discard the garlic afterwards.

2. Heat the oil in the pot over medium heat.

3. Add and stir all of the remaining ingredients, except the zucchini, into the pot. Cover the pot, lower the temperature to low and let the ingredients simmer for 5-6 hours. Unless using a crock pot or pressure cooker, make sure to stir the sauce at least once every 30 minutes while simmering, to prevent any sticking or burning on the bottom of the pot.

4. Approximately 60 minutes before removing the sauce from the heat, add the sliced zucchini.

5. Serve this sauce as is, over a slice of Italian Bread or over pasta, tortellini, ravioli, or use it in a variety of dishes such as: lasagna, chicken or eggplant Parmesan, zucchini pasta, etc.

6. Store the leftovers in the freezer, using a freezer-safe baggie or container with a tight fitting lid.

✧ ✧ ✧

ℰ⌒ VARIATIONS ⌒℥

ℋINTS

❦ Taste the sauce after the first 2-3 hours or so of simmering, and add more spice if you desire. I will usually stir an additional ½ cup red wine into the sauce at this time.

❦ This recipe also tastes superb with just a smidgen of grated hard cheese, such as Parmesan cheese, added on top when serving.

❦ One of the best parts about this grand recipe is that it produces a large batch of sauce. Therefore, it provides for lots of leftovers that can easily be stored in several freezer-safe baggies or containers, and used for several quick meals at another time.

✧ For a yummy and more nutritious meal, serve this sauce with naturally sweet and savory Spaghetti Squash, instead of pasta or bread. Easy to prepare, low in fat and calories, spaghetti squash is filled with natural vitamins that help protect against heart disease and Type 2 Diabetes, so how could you go wrong? About 90 minutes before the Tomato Sauce has finished simmering, preheat the oven to 350° Fahrenheit. Poke holes all over the squash with a fork or knife, and then place it onto a cookie sheet. Cook it in the oven for 60-70 minutes. Once the squash is tender, remove it from the oven and cut the squash in half lengthwise. Remove any seeds and then using a fork, scrape the internal flesh into a bowl. (It should 'shred' into the shape of spaghetti.) Serve it along side of the sauce or ladle the sauce on top of the squash and serve.

✧ Omit the meats and add more vegetables (e.g. 1 cup sliced mushrooms, 1 cup finely chopped spinach, 1 green pepper, seeded and diced, an extra zucchini and 2 tomatoes, previously seeded and diced).

Yammin Ham

Yammin Ham is loaded with homemade goodness. Sweet, healthy, and easy, this recipe is filled with an aroma that may cause your family to joyfully salivate in anticipation of a great meal to come. That luscious scent may also cause a couple family members to attempt to sneak into the kitchen for just a little taste. Oh but you know that they must wait, so laugh while informing them that dinner shall be ready soon and to go outside and play in the meantime.

✧

TIP:

♥ *Yams have no fat, and are as sweet as sugar – just not as fattening. Although similar in flavor to one of the oldest vegetables on earth, the sweet potato, yams are filled with Vitamin B6 that helps to boost metabolisms and keep one active. On the other hand, sweet potatoes are filled with Vitamin A, which is good for our eyes. Whichever your family prefers, know that these wonderfully healthy foods are low in calories, high in fiber, and loaded with potassium.*

Preheat oven to 325° Fahrenheit   **Serves 4-6**

1-2 tablespoons butter or margarine

1-2 tablespoons pure maple syrup or 2 teaspoons pure maple extract

1 large uncooked slice of ham, at least 1-inch thick (1-1½ pounds)

1 small can unsweetened, sliced pineapples, or 4-6 half inch slices fresh pineapple

¼ cup dark brown sugar

4-5 medium yams,

¼ teaspoon nutmeg

Pinch of cinnamon

1. Melt the butter in the bottom of a large skillet or pan and then drizzle the maple syrup or extract on top of the butter. Add the ham slice, and then brown each side for about 2-3 minutes per side.

2. Once browned, remove the ham from the skillet and place it into a large casserole dish or deep pan, and then cover it with the lid or a piece of tinfoil. (Do not discard the ham drippings remaining in the skillet; just put the skillet aside for now.)

3. Add about ¾ cup of water to the casserole dish, and then add the pineapple slices and juice on top of the ham. Cover these ingredients with tinfoil and slow bake the ham for about 100-110 minutes.

4. An hour before the ham has completed baking, wash and peel the yams thoroughly, and then boil them in a large pot filled with warm water until they just begin to soften. Remove the yams from the heat and set aside.

5. Approximately 30 minutes before the ham has finished baking, heat the drippings over medium heat. Once the drippings are hot, lower the heat to low.

6. Cut each boiled yam into four or five pieces and add them to the heated drippings. Sprinkle the yams with the brown sugar and spices and then cook them slowly at low heat, turning them over often, until browned on both sides; then remove from the heat. If necessary, cover the dish in tinfoil until serving.

7. Remove the ham from the oven, and divide the ham and yams between individual serving plates and store any leftovers covered in the refrigerator.

✧ ✧ ✧

✐ VARIATION ✐

✧ Uh oh, no time for a long cooking process, everyone is hungry now! You know a snack will ruin their appetite, so if you wish to speed up the cooking process, use leftover or pre-cooked ham. Heat it in the pan, add the pineapples and then cover the pan and allow all to simmer at a low heat for about 20 minutes. In the meantime, boil the yams until tender and cut them into bite-sized pieces. Remove the meat and pineapples from the pan, and add the yams and spice to the pan and proceed accordingly.

Shanky Soup

A good and hearty soup, perfect for replacing the quick fix of canned varieties. Sure, those canned soups are okay, but most varieties won't be cherished, remembered or requested at another date. Plus, when you can make your own savory soups, you can freeze the extras for another meal. Besides with the cost of food constantly rising, one can of soup only feeds 1-2 people, while homemade varieties will feed many.

✧

TIP:

♥ *Believe it or not, beans are actually a fruit; in fact, they are some of the healthiest of all fruits. Although low in calories, beans are high in proteins, fiber and vitamins. Plus when served regularly (a few days per week) beans have been found to curb hunger, thus, they help to control unwanted weight gain.*

✧

1 large, (or 2 small) meaty ham shank

1½ cups dry pinto beans

1½ cups dry, red kidney beans

1½ cups dry navy beans

1½ cups dry black eyed beans

One 15-ounce can garbanzo beans, drained (optional)

1 large onion, thinly sliced

3 Cloves garlic finely diced or 1 tablespoon minced garlic

1 Small bunch celery, chopped or left whole, bottoms trimmed off

¼ cup chopped fresh parsley

1. Strain the liquid from the canned beans and then pour all of the beans into a large soup pot or crock-pot.

2. Make a bouquet garni by tying the parsley and celery together with a string, or placing them in the toe of an old nylon stocking. (Cut off the excess nylon for another use.)

3. Add all of the remaining ingredients, except the garlic, to the pot, and fill the pot with warm water to just below the rim.

4. Bring all ingredients to a boil over medium high heat. Once the soup begins to boil, skim the scum from the top of the water, and then add the garlic to the soup.

5. Cover the pot and lower the heat to low medium or to a simmer (mild slow boil). Allow all ingredients to simmer for 6-8 hours or until the meat pulls away from the bones and the beans are tender.

6. Remove the bouquet garni from the pot and discard it. Remove the shank bones and scrape any remaining meat on the bones back into the soup. Discard the bones. (These bones are not good for pets, as they may splinter in the mouth or belly of your pet.)

7. Serve hot and store the leftovers covered in the refrigerator or freeze the leftovers in a freezer-safe bag or container with a tightly fitting lid.

HINT

Many say that soaking the beans in warm water overnight will help soften them. This is correct when wanting to use the beans in many quickly prepared dishes. However for this soup, soaking of the dry beans is not necessary.

Steak Break

Growing up, we weren't wealthy, but occasionally my family ate as if we were. Every now and then my mom would make steak for dinner, even though we were on a tight budget. I savored the luscious flavor of a tender and juicy piece of meat, thinly sliced for ease of a child's butter knife to cut into. But it wasn't until years later, when I was in college, that a craving for those thinly sliced pieces of steak overtook my senses; so I called mom for her recipe. As I described it she laughed out loud, while referring to it as her Steak Break recipe. *"Steak Break, huh?"* She cheerfully informed me that the recipe I so fondly remembered and craved was actually for London Broil; a large slab of beef that tasted just like steak, but that didn't break the budget.

✧

Serves 5-6

1½ pounds London Broil (about 1-inch thick)

2 tablespoons Worcestershire Sauce

1-2 teaspoons minced garlic

Sea Salt to taste

1. Melt 2 tablespoons of butter or canola-based butter spread in a large frying pan over medium heat.
2. Raise the heat under the pan just a tiny bit, but not to medium high heat.
3. Place the piece of meat into the pan, distribute the Worcestershire sauce, garlic and Sea salt all over the top of the meat.
4. Cook or grill the meat for approximately 7 minutes per side. (The center should be nice and pink, but not raw.)

5. Remove the meat from the pan, and then slice the meat against the grain, into thin pieces. Serve with baked potatoes and a freshly steamed veggie. (If you have a small family, only slice enough to serve for one meal. Average serving is 4-6 slices per person depending on age.)

6. Store leftovers covered tightly with tin foil or wrap the remaining meat in plastic wrap and place into a freezer-safe bag and freeze for another meal later in the month.

✧ ✦ ✧

ꕥ VARIATION ꕥ

✦ Marinate the London Broil overnight in 1 cup of Teriyaki Sauce, mixed with 1 cup of fresh cranberries or fresh chopped pineapples. The next evening, simply grill/cook it accordingly and serve with the fruit and sauce on top of each serving.

Cool Cucumber Salmon

According to nutritionists, we all need at least two servings of fish per week, if not more, to maintain healthy bodies and clear minds. Fish, such as salmon or tuna, are filled with omega 3 fatty acids, a good type of fat, which helps promote healthy hearts while reducing inflammations. Also, research has shown that salmon is a source of "brain food" helping to promote memory, focus, and attention. Furthermore, when fish is prepared properly, the taste can fill the senses with a lovely, soothing essence, that swirls around your tongue in pure palatable pleasure.

✧

TIP:

♥ *Cucumbers, a natural diuretic, are also known to help lower a body's temperature resulting from a fever. They help promote healthy bones, and can even help to eliminate external bodily inflammations, especially around tired eyes or swelling caused from a bug bite.*

Preheat oven to 375° Fahrenheit   **Serves 4-6**

1½ pounds salmon, cut into 4-6 pieces

1 Tablespoon canola-based butter spread

1 teaspoon dill

1 teaspoon minced garlic

1. Place the salmon onto a large piece of tinfoil. Then spread the butter and the garlic on top of each piece and then sprinkle the dill on top of the garlic.

2. Wrap tinfoil completely around each salmon piece, and then tightly twist the side edges of the foil to seal. Bake the salmon pieces for 35 minutes or until all of the flesh turns pink.

3. Remove the salmon from the oven, drain the juice and allow it to cool to room temperature or refrigerate until cold.

Cucumber Sauce

2 tablespoons mayonnaise

⅓ cup sour cream

⅓ cup plain yogurt

1 English cucumber, peeled

2 tablespoons fresh squeezed lemon juice

A dash each of Sea salt, white pepper (if available, if not black pepper is fine),

A pinch of dill to taste

4. To Prepare the Cucumber Sauce shred the cucumber in a food processor or grater and then scrape the shreds into a medium sized bowl. Add the remaining sauce ingredients to the shredded cucumber and then using a large spoon or fork gently stir the ingredients until thoroughly incorporated.

5. Serve each piece of salmon with a couple dollops of the cucumber sauce on top; accompanied by a fresh fruit salad on the side.

Hot Lemony Delight

Lemons are filled with Vitamin C, as well as various agents that help to build our immune systems and fight off colds and infections. Thus, when combined with the nutrients of fish, it is as if you are offering a plate of fresh wholesome health to your family, in addition to lots of mouth-watering flavor.

✧

Preheat oven to 350° Fahrenheit	Serves 4-5

1¼ pounds tilapia, cod, sole, halibut, tuna, bass or trout, salmon

4-5 teaspoons butter canola spread

¼ teaspoon dill

¾ teaspoon minced garlic

1 lemon, cut in half and pitted

Sauce:

½ cup fresh squeezed lemon juice

1 cup homemade chicken broth

2 tablespoons cornstarch

1 bunch scallions, bulbs diced

Pinch of dill

Pinch of parsley

2-3 tablespoon honey

1. Place the fish onto a large piece of tin foil, spread it with the butter, then spread the garlic onto the butter. Sprinkle the top of the fish with the dill and then squeeze the lemon's juice all over the fish.

2. Tightly wrap the fish in tin foil, and then twist the foil's edges tightly together to seal. Bake the fish for 40-45 minutes.

3. Prepare the sauce 10-15 minutes before the fish is done, by thoroughly mixing the juice, broth, diced scallion bulbs and cornstarch into a saucepan.

4. Stirring constantly, heat the sauce over medium heat, until it just begins to thicken.

5. Add the remaining ingredients to the saucepan and continue constantly stirring until the sauce is thick. Remove from the heat and momentarily put aside.

6. Remove the fish from the oven, unwrap the foil and then divide the fish between serving plates. (Adjust serving sizes according to the size and age of each person being served.)

7. Drizzle the sauce over each serving and serve. This dish pairs beautifully with rice for a purely nutritional, tasty meal.

Bobbing with Kabobs

Sometimes, kids, just as adults, need a change of pace to help them enjoy the diversity of foods. With this in mind, adding a smidgen of pizzazz into your favorite, everyday foods with a bit of appetizing creativity can increase their appeal. Kabobs don't just offer a grand assortment of diverse fresh flavors cooked on a stick; they offer a splendid way to jazz up your basic meals into ones that will induce memories of mingling flavors and colors. Plus, this recipe may just cause those little ones' heads bobble up and down with happiness, as their palate relishes the marvelous mingling of fresh flavors.

✧

Serves 3-4

1 cup teriyaki sauce

1 teaspoon minced garlic

Juice from ½ an orange

Juice from ½ a lemon

2-3 tablespoons finely diced scallions

2 zucchini, sliced into half inch pieces

Pinch of dry ginger

2 small to medium Vidalia or sweet onions cut into wedges

2½ navel oranges, peeled and sectioned

1 plus pound large shrimp, fresh or frozen, thawed, shelled, washed and deveined

1. Heat the grill to medium heat. (If you do not have a grill, these can also be broiled.)

2. Make the teriyaki sauce by mixing the lemon and orange juices, scallions, ginger and garlic together in a bowl and then pour a small amount in a small bowl for basting the kabobs with, and set the other bowl aside to serve with the kabobs.

3. Thread the remaining ingredients onto 6-8 skewers, alternating the ingredients by their color.

4. Brush each ingredient with the teriyaki sauce and place the kabobs on the grill. Occasionally brush the sauce onto the kabobs until the shrimp is thoroughly cooked and the vegetables are tender and crisp, about 20 minutes.

5. Place a couple of tablespoons of the extra sauce into little individual bowls or onto the side of each serving plate and serve the kabobs hot, over rice or next to a baked potato.

HINT

If broiling these Kabobs, line a cookies sheet with tin foil. Place the kabobs on the foil and proceed accordingly. Make sure to turn the kabobs over once or twice to ensure that both sides are cooked thoroughly.

✧ ✧ ✧

❧ VARIATION ❧

✧ Substitute large chunks of poultry pieces, steak or pork pieces, large scallops or raw lobster meat for the shrimp.

Fresh and Sassy Salad

A beautiful combination of colors, that promotes flavor,
health and fun with each bite.

Serves 3-4

4 cups fresh spinach, washed
thoroughly and chopped into
bite size pieces

½ cantaloupe and/or honeydew,
seeded and scooped into little
balls

1 plus cup freshly sliced
strawberries

1 avocado, diced

½ cup chopped almonds or
macadamia nuts (optional)

¾ cup fresh fruits i.e. berries,
sliced kiwi, pomegranate seeds,
etc.

¼ cup coconut for topping
(optional)

4-ounces grated Monterey or
Feta cheese (optional)

Dressing

¼ cup raspberry flavored white
wine vinegar

¼ cup olive oil

2 tablespoons honey

¼ cup raspberry or strawberry
preserves

HINT

When using fruit preserves it is best to use all-fruit or sugar-free
preserves for maximum flavor and health.

1. Have all fresh ingredients washed, sliced and ready to be used.

2. In a bowl thoroughly blend together the preserves, vinegar, oil and honey; and set aside.

3. Divide the spinach evenly among serving plates, and then top each with the cantaloupe balls and sliced strawberries.

4. Drizzle a little bit of the dressing over of each plateful of salad.

5. Sprinkle individual salads with nuts, a few berries and some coconut and serve.

✦ ✦ ✦

✐ VARIATIONS ✐

✦ Add 1 teaspoon lemon juice to the dressing before blending the ingredients.

✦ Replace the cantaloupe and strawberries with 2 sweet apples and 1 pear, both peeled and diced and substitute pure maple syrup for the fruit preserves in the dressing.

✦ Substitute 1 cup of diced papaya and/or mangos for the cantaloupe and proceed accordingly.

Layers of Pleasures Salad

I refer to this as a glorified Taco Salad, for it is full of many more flavors than just some beans, spiced ground beef, cheese, lettuce and tomato chunks. Presented in colorful layers, it's the mingling of ingredients and spices that will make this fabulous salad a household favorite; as it tastes even better than it looks. Just remember, one serving per person is enough, more is too much.

✧

TIPS:

 Another important factor about Beans is that they are naturally filled with good energy enhancing carbohydrates and Vitamin B6, plus a dose of bone strengthening calcium, potassium, and magnesium. Additionally, due to the high amounts of proteins and fiber in beans, studies have shown that eating beans regularly reduces the risk of developing heart disease, cancer, diabetes and possibly cancer.

 Avocados are filled with a good type of fat, lots of fiber and potassium. Though they are loaded with calories, just a little bit packs a huge punch in flavor and health. Additionally avocados have been found to help those suffering from Diabetes.

✧

Serves 6-7

1 head iceberg lettuce, shredded

1 pound ground beef, cooked until browned

1 medium red onion, diced or ½ cup diced scallions

One 15-ounce can refried Pinto Beans

One 15-ounce can Black beans, thoroughly drained

One 15-ounce can Garbanzo beans, thoroughly drained

One 15-ounce can Kidney beans, thoroughly drained

1 small can sliced jalapenos or green chilies,

1 cup diced tomato

1½-2 avocados peeled, pitted, and diced

⅓ cup sour cream

¼ cup plain yogurt

12-16 ounces grated Sharp Cheddar or Marbled cheese

1½ cups tomato or pineapple salsa (page 38)

One 4-ounce can sliced black olives, thoroughly drained

1. In a large bowl, spread ⅓ of the shredded lettuce onto the bottom of the bowl.

2. Warm the refried beans, and then spread them on top of the lettuce. Add half of the previously cooked warm meat on top of the refried beans, and then sprinkle one third of the cheese on top of the meat. Spread the whole can of black beans on top of this.

3. After spreading the black beans, spread the diced onions on top, then add the garbanzo beans, then the sliced jalapenos, the remaining warm beef, more lettuce, and then the tomatoes. Top this layer with the remaining cheese, and then add the kidney beans, avocados, and the remaining lettuce.

4. Once this part of the layering process is complete, spread ¾ cup or more of preferred salsa all over the top of the salad.

5. Thoroughly mix the sour cream and yogurt together and then gently spread this mixture on top of the sauce.

6. Sprinkle the sliced olives all over the top and serve.

7. Store the leftover tightly covered in the refrigerator.

✧ ✧ ✧

✐ VARIATION ✐

✧ Substitute the ground beef with 1 pound of previously cooked shredded beef, chicken, turkey or pulled pork

Pineapple Salsa

To jazz up various foods, why not try this tasty alternative to common salsa? It is especially scrumptious when served on top of homemade chicken burritos, tacos, or when used to enhance a basic chicken or fish dish such as grilled halibut and rice.

✧

Makes about 6 servings

2 medium sized oranges, peeled and cut into 1 inch pieces or one 11-ounce can mandarin oranges, drained, rinsed with water

1½ cups freshly chopped pineapple or one 20-ounce can unsweetened chopped pineapple, drained

1 tablespoon finely diced scallion or red onion

2 teaspoons diced jalapeno or 1 jalapeno, seeded and finely chopped (optional)

3 tablespoons lime or lemon juice

Scant ¼ cup 100% orange juice

1. Mix all of the ingredients thoroughly together in a medium sized bowl.

2. Cover the bowl with plastic wrap and refrigerate for at least 30 minutes or until serving. *If using with other recipes, remove this salsa from the refrigerator while preparing the meat, poultry or fish, stir it a few times and set aside until serving.

✧ ✧ ✧

🐑 HINT

🐑 If adding to the Layers of Pleasures salad, you may want to omit the jalapenos from this recipe.

⌇ VARIATIONS ⌇

✧ This salsa, though spicy, is a fabulous salad when served on top of a bowl of shredded or chopped green leaves, such as spinach or lettuce.

✧ For a terrific flavor, substitute 1-2 tablespoons of Teriyaki sauce for the jalapenos when using this salsa to spice up grilled poultry or fish.

HINT

For maximum flavor, it is always best to bring a chilled food complement to room temperature prior to serving with hot food.

Chunky Salsa Dance

Yes, the marvelous blend of ingredients may just inspire you and the kids to tap your feet and dance to the flavors of edible joy.

✧

Makes about 1 cup

1 large tomato, seeded and finely diced

½ cucumber, finely diced

2 tablespoons fresh chopped or 1 teaspoon dry cilantro

1 jalapeno, diced or one 4-ounce can diced jalapenos

2-3 tablespoons diced onion or scallion

½ teaspoon minced garlic (more or less depending on personal preference)

½ teaspoon oregano

1 teaspoon hot sauce

Pinch of cumin

Mix all ingredients together and put in a bowl for immediate use or refrigerate for later.

Shrimp Salad

❦

You do not have to live by the sea to enjoy the savory flavors of seafood. Even if you reside high upon a mountain, or in a sandy desert, you and your family can still enjoy the benefits (high in protein, low in fat) and flavor of seafood every now and then, even when on a budget.

✧

TIP:

💜 *Celery, a common vegetable, doesn't just taste fresh and natural; it is packed with potassium, vitamin B, and folic acid that help to promote energy. Plus, it has been found to be a natural diuretic, helps to lower high blood pressure and was used centuries ago as a stress relieving food. And because celery contains a natural amount of salt, it makes a super substitute for salty snacks, and eliminates the need to add extra amounts of salt to soups and various salads to punctuate the flavor.*

Serves 3-4

16-20 ounces medium shrimp, cooked, peeled, and deveined

¾ cup diced celery

¾ cup diced red onion

1 teaspoon dill

1 teaspoon minced garlic

Pinch or two Bay Seafood Seasoning

1 tablespoon freshly squeezed lemon juice

3-4 tablespoons mayonnaise (only enough to moisten the salad, as no more is needed)

🍳HINT

🍷 Frozen shrimp works fine in this recipe. To quickly thaw the shrimp, place the required amount into a large bowl, and fill it with very cold water. Allow the shrimp to thaw in the water about 30 minutes. You may wish to change the water once or twice until the shrimp are completely thawed.

1. Place all ingredients into a bowl and gently mix together.
2. Allow the salad ingredients to blend for about half an hour, if time allows.
3. Serve as is, or with cucumber and/or tomato wedges served on the side.

✧ ✧ ✧

⌒ VARIATION ⌒

✧ This can also be prepared with a combination of freshly cooked Lobster, bay scallops, and/or crabmeat.

Corny Bean Salad

This is a wonderful complement to various foods ranging from cheese omelets to a beef roast, to enchiladas. Fabulously delish as a snack too, but especially so when served with a side of sliced cucumbers instead of tortilla chips.

✧

One 14-ounce can black beans, thoroughly drained

One 14-ounce can corn kernels, or 2 cups frozen corn kernels thawed and drained

1 tomato, seeded and diced

⅓ cup finely diced onion (preferably a red onion)

Scant teaspoon minced garlic

½ teaspoon dry cilantro

2 tablespoons fresh diced parsley or 1 teaspoon dry parsley

2-3 tablespoons oil based Italian Dressing

1 tablespoon fresh lemon juice

1 teaspoon minced jalapeno or red chili pepper, optional

1. Place the drained black beans and corn into a medium size bowl.
2. Add all remaining ingredients to the beans and mix thoroughly.
3. Cover the bowl with plastic wrap and refrigerate until serving.

Royal Salad

Not only is this recipe perfect for all the little kings and queens in your household; but it is also one of the most versatile recipes I have created to date. It can be adjusted to meet individual family preferences, and takes into account ingredients that are available locally. So just pick out your family's favorite fruits and begin inserting them in-between the smooth, comforting layers of honey-sweetened yogurt.

✧

TIPS:

♥ *Hey mom and dad, a little extra serving of this food is okay! People have known for centuries that yogurt is a "good for you" food that helps sustain good bacteria in our bodies, is high in proteins that help build muscles while curbing appetites, and is filled with natural calcium that helps build strong bones and teeth.*

♥ *And honey, although high in calories is known as one of Mother Nature's greatest healers. It helps to temper various stomach ailments, build up our immune systems, sooth a sore throat, and repair damaged tissue. In addition, it can help fight infections and inflammations, and can even help heal a cut or scratch. So with all of these good benefits, why would you choose sugar to sweeten various foods, (tea, yogurt, cereals) when honey is so much better for you and your children?*

♥ *Kiwi actually contain much more Vitamin C than oranges, has as much potassium as a banana, are filled with beta-carotenes that help to build our immunity systems, and some studies have found that they are good for our respiratory systems and may help to alleviate wheezing while sleeping.*

HINT

🐝 To toast nuts, preheat the oven to 350° Fahrenheit. Line the nuts evenly on a cookie sheet, and bake for 10-12 minutes or until golden brown. Make sure to either shake the pan a couple times to turn the nuts or flip them over with a metal spatula, ensuring that both sides get toasted. For small amounts, you can also evenly spread nuts on a small piece of tinfoil and bake in a toaster oven for 2-3 minutes or until golden brown.

Serves 5-6 as a meal, 10-12 as a snack

One 32-ounce container plain yogurt

¼ cup of honey

½ cup pomegranate juice (optional)

1½ cups chopped papaya or mango

1 cup sliced strawberries

1½ cups freshly chopped pineapple or pineapple canned in unsweetened juice

2 kiwis, peeled and thinly sliced

1 cup blueberries, fresh or freshly frozen and thawed

1 cup pitted dark cherries or blackberries fresh or freshly frozen and thawed

1-2 bananas, thinly sliced and added when serving)

1 cup toasted almonds or walnuts (see HINT)

1. Mix the yogurt and honey thoroughly together.

2. Place the papaya in the bottom of a bowl (clear glass if you've got one), and then the strawberries on top of the papaya.

3. Spread ¼ of the yogurt mixture all over the top of the fruit.

4. Drizzle 2 tablespoons of pomegranate juice (if using) on top of the yogurt.

5. Distribute the pineapple chunks on top of this layer, and then spread another ¼ of the yogurt and another 2 tablespoons of pomegranate on top of this.

6. Add the kiwi slices around the sides of the bowl, as if they are standing up looking out from the bowl and then sprinkle the blueberries into the center of the bowl. Spread another ¼ of the yogurt on top of the blueberries and 2 more tablespoons of pomegranate juice on top of the yogurt.

7. Add the cherries, sliced bananas, the remaining yogurt and juice and end the layering process by sprinkling the nuts all over the top. Serve immediately or cover with plastic wrap and store in the refrigerator. This should stay fresh when covered tightly and placed in the refrigerator for 2-3 days.

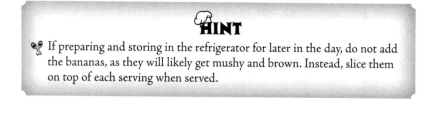

HINT

If preparing and storing in the refrigerator for later in the day, do not add the bananas, as they will likely get mushy and brown. Instead, slice them on top of each serving when served.

O'Cucumion Salad

When making better food choices for your family, it is always best to offer fresh fruit or leafy salad instead of a second helping of food. Yet, sometimes just looking at that same old bowl of fruit or salad can discourage your loved ones from enjoying its benefits. The same old stuff really can get boring, right? Of course it can! So what do you do; you easily prepare a different type of salad or fruit bowl, making such offerings versatile, tasty, and memorable, such as this recipe.

✧

TIP:

💗 *Onions are filled with endless healing properties. They help to fight infections, colds, bodily inflammations, the onset of diabetes, osteoporosis, prevent blood clots, lower blood pressure, and have even been found to help treat asthma.*

✧

HINT

When purchasing onions, always pick the smallest ones from the pile. They supply a much more pungent flavor than the larger ones. Also, to prevent the onset of tears (caused by natural gases that are released when the onion cut into), you can peel the onion under very cold water or next to running water and then slice accordingly. Or slice it by a steaming pot of water or broth; or, and yes this works—chop, slice or dice an onion next to a burning candle. The flame will attract the gas and detour it away from your eyes! Also, wash your hands well with soap and water immediately after slicing, chopping or dicing an onion to prevent the gas and juice from accidentally getting in your eyes.

Serve 3-4

2 cucumbers

1 small red onion

1½ cups water

½ cup white or rice wine vinegar

½ teaspoon seasoned salt (see below for recipe)

1½ teaspoons sugar, or honey or 1 teaspoon sugar substitute

1. Peel and thinly slice cucumbers. Slices should be about ⅛-inch thick.

2. Peel and thinly slice the onion, again about ⅛-inch thick slices.

3. In a small bowl or jar with a tight fitting lid, stir or shake the water, vinegar, sugar and seasoned salt. Once thoroughly mixed, pour mixture all over the vegetables and chill for 1 hour.

Seasoned Salt

Superb for enhancing the natural flavor of meat, poultry or fish.

1 teaspoon Sea salt

¼ teaspoon white pepper

¼ teaspoon black pepper

¼ teaspoon garlic powder

⅛ teaspoon oregano

¼ teaspoon paprika

¼ teaspoon celery seed

Mix ingredients together and store in a tightly sealed jar or plastic container in the refrigerator until serving.

Beet It

❧

Due to the fact that the purplish magenta color of beets is gorgeous, and that they are indeed naturally sweet to taste, how could you deny your loved ones such a marvelously healthful and flavorful vegetable? Readily available throughout the world, pre-cooked varieties can usually be found in the produce department of most grocery stores. (Just make sure that the only ingredients listed on the package are beets and water.) Beets naturally contain salt and sugar, thus additional amounts are not necessary. While the packaged varieties are fine, if you choose to grow your own or purchase them raw, see directions for cooking them after this salad's recipe.

✧

TIP:

♥ *Beets offer another super source of antioxidants that help prevent various ailments, such as colds, viruses, heart problems and various cancers, such as Colon Cancer. They are also a natural source of folic acid, which helps promote good metabolisms and increase energy levels. Plus, the fresh green leaves provide a delicious source of vitamins and can be prepared just as you would spinach.*

✧

Serves 4

4 previous cooked red beets

½ red onion finely diced or
1 bunch of scallions, with the
white bulb thinly sliced or diced

½ cup finely diced celery

¼ cup, plus a tablespoon Low
Fat Ranch, Blue Cheese or
Vinaigrette Salad Dressing

¼ cup grated Parmesan and/or
Romano Cheese (optional)

1. Thinly slice the beets or grate them in a food processor and then pour them into a bowl.

2. Add the remaining ingredients and gently stir the salad to evenly distribute the dressing.

3. Refrigerate until serving, and then serve with a sprinkling of suggested cheese if desired.

TO COOK RAW BEETS

Trim most of the stem away, leaving about 1½ inches on the top of the bulb and the roots intact. Wash the leaves; pat them dry with a paper towel and store in the refrigerator. Gently wash the beet bulb, but do not peel off the outer layer of skin as both the top stem and root get removed after cooking. Fill a large pot with warm water and 1 tablespoon of vinegar. The vinegar helps to maintain the natural pretty color of the beets. Place the beets (one pound is equivalent to 3-4 servings) into the warm water bath and boil them at medium high heat until tender and easily pierced, or about 15-20 minutes. Do not over boil the beets as they could get too mushy and will only work to prepare a soup such as Borscht. Remove the beets from the water, trim off the remaining stems and roots, and gently rub off the outer layer with gloved hands or a paper towel. Allow the beets to cool, and then you can slice, grate or julienne them into little sticks. Beets are a wonderful addition to salads, stews and roasted veggies.

Tropical French Toast

Long ago on a cold, rainy evening, I got a craving for something sweet, warm and relatively healthy, as it had been a long day. Fortunately I remembered this recipe from decades past when I used to stay at my grandmother's. Oh my, as the aroma flowed around me, the memories of her small apartment came rushing back. And, then the phone rang, interrupting my path to the past. How the scent of comforting warmth flowed across 2,000 miles I may never know, but it was my Dad on the phone and he was curious if I had his mother's special recipe for French toast. It was cold and rainy at his home too and he had the same craving. Evidently good homemade food isn't just remembered and reproduced, it brings comfort to those you love, even when you are miles apart.

✧

Serves 2-4

4 eggs

2 tablespoons milk

1 teaspoon maple extract

¼ teaspoon cinnamon

4 pieces raisin or whole grain bread

3 tablespoons cream cheese, softened

2 small bananas, thinly sliced

6- 8 strawberries, thinly sliced

1 small can unsweetened pineapple slices or 4, half-inch slices fresh pineapple

1. Mix the eggs, milk, maple extract and cinnamon thoroughly together.
2. Whip the cream cheese to soften it, or soften it slightly in the microwave so that it can be easily spread.

3. Gently spread a small amount of the soft cream cheese onto each slice of bread.

4. Evenly distribute the bananas and strawberries on top of the cream cheese and then fold each piece in half. You may wish to use a tiny bit of extra cream cheese to pinch and seal the half together.

5. Grease a large (non-stick preferably) frying pan well with pan spray, butter or margarine.

6. Dip each piece of bread individually into the egg mixture, and coat both sides.

7. Fry each piece until just golden on both sides.

8. Top each with a thin pineapple slice and then distribute the remaining eggs over each piece of golden toast. Immediately flip the toast and fruit over to cook the eggs and warm the pineapple. Allow this side to cook for 10-15 seconds, but not longer.

9. Serve each with a small drizzle of warmed maple syrup, a pinch of cinnamon sugar or a small dollop of vanilla yogurt on top of each serving.

HINT

Remember not to drown the toast in Maple Syrup; a tablespoon per piece is a sufficient amount, for the favored maple flavor has already been added.

Peachy Sweet Cakes and Eggs

Pleasant and easy, this fabulous dish can be served any time of the day. Wow, breakfast food for dinner is definitely cool, sweetly nutritious and satisfying for even the fussiest of eaters.

✧

Makes 20-24 mini cakes   **(3-4 cakes per serving)**

HINT

❧ Although the directions are long, this only takes about 20-30 minutes to prepare and serve.

¾ pound yams or sweet potatoes

1½ cups flour

3½ teaspoons baking powder

1 teaspoon Sea salt

½ teaspoon cinnamon

¼ teaspoon ground nutmeg

½ teaspoon ginger

¼ cup (½ stick) butter or margarine, melted

½ cup raisins presoaked and patted dry (optional)

2 eggs, beaten

1½ cups milk

2 cups freshly frozen sliced peaches, thawed and drained

2-3 tablespoons reserved peach juice

8 eggs

3 tablespoons milk

4 scallions, diced

HIGH ALTITUDE TIP   Add 2 more tablespoons flour and extra tablespoon milk to the batter. Proceed according.

---

1. Peel, wash and cut the yams into pieces. Completely cover the yams in warm water in a saucepan and boil until tender and easily pierced with a knife or fork.

2. While the yams are boiling, sift together the flour, baking powder and spices into a medium sized bowl.

3. In another bowl, thoroughly mix together the 8 eggs, diced scallions, salt and pepper and set aside.

4. Once the yams are tender, drain all the water from then saucepan and place them into a separate bowl.

5. Add the 2 beaten eggs, milk and melted butter to the potatoes and mash all ingredients together using an old-fashioned potato masher or a hand mixer. Mash the ingredients until smooth, but do not beat them until starchy.

6. Lightly fold the potato mixture into the flour mixture until all ingredients are thoroughly incorporated.

7. Grease a non-stick griddle or pan with pan spray and then heat it over medium high heat.

8. Working rapidly, drop individual rounded tablespoon of the potato batter onto the prepared pan and once the top begins to bubble flip each cake over and cook the other side until golden.

9. Remove the individual cakes from the pan, place them on a plate, cover the plate lightly with tin foil and repeat until all batter has been used.

10. Once all the batter has been used, lower the heat to medium, re-grease the pan and scramble the eggs.

11. Warm the peaches and reserved juice in a saucepan over medium heat or in the microwave.

12. Place 2-3 cakes upon each serving plate, pour the peaches and juice on top of the cakes distribute the eggs accordingly and serve while all is still very warm-hot.

13. Wrap the excess cakes in plastic wrap, and then place them into a baggie and refrigerate or freeze.

Modeling for a Better Life

❧

Children are born with openness to all that they encounter. Naturally they develop many of their habits and behaviors by modeling those around them, in an attempt to be like them. You, as their parents, are the ones who unconsciously institute many of their behaviors, likes and dislikes from the very moment that your babies are born. As they grow, they begin to model your actions, sometimes your words, and often your habits. For instance, if you read lots of books, or curse a lot, they are likely to do the same. Likewise, if you prefer to eat a diet full of pizza, subs, fast and fried food, salt and sugar-saturated food, and artificially flavored snacks and beverages, they will too. However, if you drink lots of water, milk, and juice, and eat lots of fruits, vegetables, and homemade food, so will they!

One of the most important things that you can do as a parent or guardian is to teach and model the importance of eating a good breakfast. An easy feat to accomplish, as all you really need to do is to eat whole grains, protein and fruit for breakfast; rather than just grabbing a cup of coffee and prepackaged sugar fix as you run out the door. You have heard many times and it is absolutely true: *"breakfast is the most important meal of the day."* It supplies nourishment to our bodies and energy to our brains, allowing both to function more productively throughout the day. An early morning sugar fix only increases the desire for more sugar, before the next meal.

As a teacher, I saw the effects that a good breakfast had on my students' behavior and their grades. Those who skipped breakfast or only ate prepackaged, sugar filled foods before school — tended to be crankier, acted out more, and had lower grades than those who actually ate a breakfast made from whole grain cereals, eggs and/or fruits. It is a fact that eating a healthy breakfast limits the desire for fattening snacks between meals, hence, it helps control unwanted weight gain. The bottom line is that when you eat a good breakfast, so will your kids. So be a good role model and eat a well-balanced breakfast, even if that means you must set the alarm clock to buzz ten minutes sooner than you have grown accustomed to.

Another issue to consider when modeling and instilling good eating habits is that kids (and adults) eat what is available to them. If a food is not available (e.g.. soda, prepackaged cookies, cakes, and chips), they cannot eat or drink it. If you no longer purchase sugarcoated cereals, artificially flavored beverages (soda and juicy drinks), salt and sugar-saturated snacks and super-sized bags of junk food, then they will not be there for them to indulge in daily. This act alone will help save funds and prevent the overeating of junk food! Basically, if it's not there, then they cannot indulge themselves in your absence. If the kids are hungry after school, you can always have a homemade snack prepared, such as cheese and fruit wraps (page 69) or yogurt mixed with fresh fruits, for them to quench their hunger with; rather than that large bag of cookies, chips or inexpensive, individually frozen foods (e.g. burritos), easily heated in the microwave. Keep in mind, that family members may at first challenge such flavorful alternatives offered in exchange for their more fattening preferences. To remedy any potential arguments or whining, just remind them that *"I love you, and these changes are made so that you have more energy to play and enjoy life with!"* This act of love will result in improved eating habits, and their waistlines will begin to shrink a little bit too. Ultimately, your children will be happier, healthier, and much more productive.

Lastly, remember that you are not always aware of what foods your kids are eating while away from home. Teachers often serve sodas, candies and cakes while celebrating a birthday or holiday. Children commonly swap food during lunch. Babysitters and neighbors like to offer treats while watching your children and grandparents are infamous for spoiling children with sweets and gifts, just because they can. When you and your family are together, at least you can provide them with good examples and control what they eat and drink

✧ ✧ ✧

TIPS:

♥ *Blueberries have been found to increase "brain power," and whole wheat or whole grain cereals and breads have been found to help kids stay more focused than sugarcoated varieties and/or plain old white bread.*

HINT

🐑 The above information does not imply that you have to completely give up on all sweet and prepackaged foods, rather to limit your family's indulgence of these foods in exchange for more nutritional ones. For instance, sugarcoated cereals may be the preferred early morning choice by your children, but not a good choice to serve on school days. These sweetened cereals hamper their ability to stay focused and retain information, while increasing their desire to snack between meals. However on the weekends, when they have lots of time to play and work off excess energy, the occasional serving of such is fine, but should be limited to the suggested serving amounts.

Papaya Bowl

Papaya a luscious, oblong fruit is commonly eaten in slices or chunks as a snack, or added to many foods such as salsas, salads, and roasts to enrich their flavor. However, did you know that once the seeds are removed, these lovely, full flavored fruits make terrific bowls to be filled with delicacies such as salads, yogurts or cereals? Papaya is best served when the skin turns yellowish to burnt orange, and is relatively firm like a ripe avocado when touched, but not too soft.

✧

TIP:

💜 *Papayas, a favorite tropical delight, are a great source of enzymes to alleviate the symptoms of an upset stomach or a slight case of indigestion.*

✧

1. Slice a papaya in half lengthwise and scoop out the seeds.

2. If the bowl is not deep enough to your liking, cut ¼-inch chunks out from the center and mix them with the cereal or store them, covered with plastic wrap, in the refrigerator for a snack later in the day.

3. Fill the fruit bowl with choice of cereal, milk and a 1-2 tablespoons of blueberries.

4. Make sure to instruct the kids to scoop some of the fruit with each spoonful, but not to dig too far down in the fruit bowl until all the cereal is gone. This way you can avoid a mess resulting from any holes accidentally poked in the fruit bowl's skin.

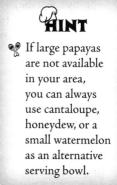

HINT

🍒 If large papayas are not available in your area, you can always use cantaloupe, honeydew, or a small watermelon as an alternative serving bowl.

Suggested Homemade Cereals

OATMEAL
(See Homemade Oatmeal on page 94)

✧

CRÈME OF RICE

This tasty, yet nutritional cereal is wonderful for children (and adults) with allergies to wheat products. And it tastes so good that even those without any dietary restrictions will still enjoy the marvelous flavor.

✧

TIP:

♥ *Brown rice has many more nutrients than white rice. White rice, although it may appear fluffier, gets washed and rinsed of its natural outer layer of bran, and a few natural vitamins, and is often covered with glucose or talc to make it appear shiny and appealing.*

Serves 2-3

1 cup brown rice, rinsed with warm water and thoroughly drained

4¼ cups milk

1 teaspoon vanilla

Pinch of salt

½ teaspoon cinnamon and/or nutmeg, (optional)

2 tablespoons butter or margarine

½ cup raisins or choice of dried fruits, blueberries, sweet dark pitted cherries. or diced and peeled fruit, such as apples, peaches or bananas.

1-2 teaspoons honey, sugar, or brown sugar (optional)

HIGH ALTITUDE TIP This recipe will take a few more minutes to cook at higher elevations. If located above 8500 ft., know that this recipe may take 25-35 minutes to cook thoroughly.

1. Place the milk and butter in a medium saucepan over medium high heat, bring to a boil. Add the rice, salt, cinnamon, and choice of fruit (withhold the bananas until serving) and stir.

2. Cover the saucepan, lower the heat to low-medium and simmer for approximately 10-12 minutes or until rice is chewy, not tough. Remove from the heat and stir in your choice of sweetener, if using.

3. Divide the cereal between bowls and serve immediately with warmed milk.

✧ ✧ ✧

❧ VARIATIONS ❧

✧ Replace the vanilla with 1 teaspoon of pure maple or almond extract.

✧ Sprinkle a handful of chopped nuts (almonds, hazelnuts, pecans, walnuts) on top of the cereal after filling individual bowls.

MUESLI CRUNCH

Due to the awesome blend of ingredients, this cereal only takes minutes to prepare, but promises to fill your loved ones with smiles and nourishment that only the heart of a parent, grandparent or caretaker can provide. Loaded with nutrients and fun flavors, this recipe is brimming with goodness and nutrients that will sustain one until the next meal; hence eliminating the urge to snack before lunch.

✧

Serves 2

1 cup plain yogurt

1 cup quick oats

½ teaspoon cinnamon

½ cup milk

1½ tablespoons sugar, honey or sugar substitute

Dash or 2 of nutmeg

1 peeled, cored, and diced Granny Smith or Pippin apple or 1 skinned and diced peach

1 tablespoon sunflower or pumpkin seeds (optional)

1-2 tablespoons chopped nuts (optional)

1-2 tablespoons fresh squeezed lemon juice

1 tablespoon pomegranate juice, (optional)

½ cup blueberries

1 sliced banana

1. Lightly combine all ingredients in the order given (except bananas and berries) into a large bowl. Cover the bowl with plastic wrap and allow the ingredients to blend together in the refrigerator overnight.
   (Do not vigorously stir the ingredients; simply combine then by folding them together once, twice at the most.)

2. The next morning, fill each papaya half or bowl with the cereal, drizzle a dash of milk on top and sprinkle with the fresh banana slices and/or berries.

Broiled Grapefruit

A long time ago, there was a Home Economics Teacher who taught a class of third graders how to prepare simple, but delicious breakfast foods. I will never forget the day she taught us how to make this wonderful recipe and my excitement as I went to bed that night, knowing that I was going to wake-up early and shock my parents by having breakfast all made up for them. Boy, were they thrilled, and my mom was delighted that there was actually no mess to clean up after. This recipe also makes a terrific after school snack, especially on chilly days.

✧

Serves 2

1 Grapefruit

2-3 teaspoons butter or butter spread

2-3 teaspoons cinnamon sugar or brown sugar cinnamon

1. On a plate or cutting board, cut the grapefruit into even halves with a serrated knife. Using the same knife, cut down and along the inside rind and in between each white membrane to section the fruit and loosen individual bites.

2. Dot the top with a small amount of butter or spread a very small amount of butter spread all over the top of each half. Sprinkle a bit of cinnamon sugar on top of each half, making sure that it lightly covers each individual section.

3. Place the halves onto a tinfoil covered toaster oven pan, and set the toaster oven temperature to broil. Broil the grapefruits for 1-2 minutes or until brown or caramelized on the top.

4. Turn the toaster oven off and remove the pan using a kitchen mitt. Serve immediately.

HINT

❧ To make brown sugar cinnamon, simply mix 2 tablespoons of brown sugar with ½ teaspoon cinnamon.

Tempering the Temperament Treats

Everyone gets cranky every now and then, especially kids. The cause may be hormonal, stress induced, peer related, or perhaps lack of sleep; but the fact remains, we all can get cranky once in a while. Fortunately, there are a few naturally sweet, calming treats that will help to temper the temperament of those you love. By the way, these are terrific recipes for modeling the proper foods to eat during stressful times, including those of your own.

✧

TIP: *Packed with a potent combination of nutrients, almonds have been found to contribute healthful benefits to each part of our bodies; including helping to eliminate bad cholesterol. Their natural oil helps to prevent pimples and blackheads and daily consumption adds a healthy glow to skin and hair. They have an amazing sweet, yet woodsy scent that has been used for centuries to calm both body and mind; and they release chemicals in our brains that help to temper crankiness while producing good feelings, positive attitudes and alert brains.*

✧

MORNING CRUNCH COCKTAIL

Per 1 serving

¼ cup whole almonds per person

8-10 ounce glass of milk per person

¼ teaspoon vanilla per person (optional)

1. Measure the ingredients into a bowl, stir and cover the bowl with plastic film.
2. Place the bowl in the refrigerator overnight, and serve for a quick breakfast the next morning. Best serve with a piece of cinnamon raisin or whole grain toast on the side.

ALMOND DELIGHT

"Oh Mom, this stuff is crisp. "Yea, good stuff Mom! Yum!"
And to think it only takes a minute to throw together.

✧

Per 1 individual serving

---

1 cup plain yogurt

1 tablespoon sliced almonds

½ banana sliced or ¼ cup pitted sweet dark cherries

1 scant tablespoon mini, semi-sweet chocolate chips

1-2 teaspoons honey

Mix all ingredient into a small bowl or container, cover with plastic wrap and refrigerate until serving.

✧ ✧ ✧

⌒ VARIATION ⌒

✧ Eliminate adding the honey and use vanilla yogurt instead of plain yogurt.

HINT

For a special effect, layer the ingredients into a glass. Begin by first mixing the honey and yogurt in a small bowl. Place half of the fruit into the bottom of a clear glass and then spoon half of the yogurt on top of the fruit. Sprinkle the mini chocolate chips on top of the yogurt, and then spoon on the remaining yogurt. Add the remaining fruit to the top of the yogurt and top it all off with the sliced almonds. Cover with plastic wrap and refrigerate until serving.

Fruit Sprtizer

One of the greatest ways to model good eating habits is to honestly stop drinking sugar – saturated and artificially flavored beverages, by replacing them with healthier choices. Sodas, including those advertised as "Diet Soda" can be compared to a devil's advocate when trying to induce and maintain weight loss. This simple, flavorful alternative supplies the same carbonated fix, tastes superb, and provides a means for getting more fruits into the bodies of those you love. The best part, once you show the kids how to prepare this awesome beverage, then they can make their own; even when you are not at home.

✧

TIP:

💗 *Researchers have found that daily consumption of sodas, juicy drinks, powdered juices and artificially flavored, sugar-saturated, prepackaged snacks, can actually pack on an extra 10 plus pounds in just one year, especially when a person doesn't get much exercise. Another of their findings indicates that artificially flavored sodas, including those advertised as 'diet soda', have a tendency to increase an appetite rather than satisfy it.*

Serves 1-2

One, 8 ounce bottle club soda

1 cup 100% fruit juice

Ice cubes, or Fruity Cubes
(page 63)

Mix all ingredients together in a glass and enjoy.

Fruity Cubes

Fruit-flavored water has become a favorite beverage for many. But, why would you waste your hard-earned funds on fruit-flavored waters, when you can make it with whole fruits or pure fruit juice so very easily and at much less of a price?

✧

A. Take ¼ – ½ cup of previously frozen fruit and thaw it until juicy in the microwave (about 1 minute). Drain the juice into a cup or small bowl and set the remaining fruit aside in the refrigerator to be mixed with yogurt or applesauce for a snack later in the day. To make ice cubes, mix the juice with enough water to fill each section of an ice cube tray. Freeze the tray until the ice cubes are solid and use when flavoring water or preparing a Fruit Spritzer.

B. Simply drop a whole berry or several tiny berries (blueberry, raspberry, strawberry, huckleberry, blackberry, gooseberry, grape, few pomegranate seeds, or a pitted dark cherry half) into each section of the ice cube tray, fill the sections with water and freeze accordingly. If using strawberries, cut the stems off, and slice each in half lengthwise and then add to the ice cube tray.

Quick Breakfast Sandwiches

Have you ever had one of those mornings when all awaken late to the day ahead? While shuffling everyone in and out of bathrooms and closets, you begin to think of what to feed your family, realizing you have no time to spare. Then you remember those frozen, prepackaged breakfast foods, which you purchased purposely for days like these. Yes, they are filling and better than nothing, but do you really want you and your children to begin the day with manufactured product; when alternatives are just as easy to prepare in advance and can be made to the preferences of individual family members?

✧

BACON AND EGG SANDWICHES

TIPS:

♥ *When serving the following sandwiches fresh out of the pan, knowing that the next meal is far ahead, why not try adding a tomato slice and/or sprouts. If your kids like it this way, super. If not, praise them for giving it a try and then immediately remove the extra veggies, so that they may enjoy their sandwich as they like it.*

♥ *To absorb more of the bacon's fat, place the bacon slices onto a plate covered with two paper towels, and then add another piece of paper towel on top of the bacon. Cook the slices in the microwave oven for 4 minutes or until brown and crisp. Once crisp, immediately remove the slices from the paper towel to prevent sticking, and set them aside on another plate.*

HINT

🍒 I have listed the cheese as optional, for some people do not like cheese on their eggs. Therefore when preparing a large batch, you may wish to only sprinkle the cheese onto half of the eggs, leaving the other half plain; and then label the sandwiches accordingly when storing to eat at another time.

Makes 6 sandwiches

6 English muffins, or 12 pieces of whole grain toast

9 large eggs or equivalent amount of liquid egg substitute

2 teaspoons finely diced onion (optional)

⅓ cup milk

A couple drops of Tabasco® or hot sauce (optional)

Sea salt and pepper to taste

8-9 pieces of cooked bacon, ham, or 6 sausage patties (or make a combination, according to personal preferences)

6 ounces of grated Cheddar or Colby cheese (optional)

Sliced tomatoes, peppers or sprouts (optional)

1. Fry the bacon (or sausage) in a pan until browned and crispy. Remove the slices from the pan and place them onto a paper towel lined plate to absorb excess grease. Remove from the paper towel and set aside on a different plate.

2. Lightly toast the bread. Butter one slice of toast per sandwich and then set all slices aside.

3. Grease a medium size frying pan with pan spray, butter or margarine and then begin to heat the pan over medium heat.

4. Crack the eggs into a bowl and beat vigorously with a wire whisk or fork while adding the milk and spices until thoroughly incorporated.

5. Pour the egg mixture into the hot frying pan and stir with a spatula until the egg mixture just begins to solidify, and then sprinkle the cheese on top of the eggs. (The eggs will cook a little when reheated, so you will want to store them moist, but not runny)

6. Cover the pan for a few seconds, allow the cheese to melt slightly and then remove the pan from the heat.

7. To assemble the sandwiches, place 1½ pieces of bacon (or a sausage patty) onto one slice of prepared bread. Scoop equal amounts of eggs onto the bacon, top with remaining slice of bread, and then cover each thoroughly in plastic wrap. Place the sandwiches into a freezer-safe bag or airtight plastic container while still warm to retain moisture and freeze up to one month.

8. To thaw, unwrap the plastic film around each sandwich, and then wrap it in a paper towel to prevent the bread from getting tough in the microwave. Heat the sandwich on high in the microwave for 60-90 seconds or until hot.

LITTLE BISCUIT SANDWICHES

No prepackaged biscuit, whether frozen or refrigerated, can compete with these divine little puffs of homemade love. Store-bought biscuits are fine and dandy, but homemade ones will be treasured and savored for generations to come. Plus, if you have little ones, you can always alter the shape of these biscuits by using different 2-3 inch straight-edge, shaped cookie cutters. Store-bought versions do not allow these little personal pleasures

✧

TIP: *If your children cannot have dairy, substitute 1 cup soy or almond milk mixed with 1 tablespoon vinegar for the buttermilk. Although yogurt can usually be used in place of buttermilk in most recipes, it does not work well in this one.*

✧

Preheat oven to 400° Fahrenheit	Makes 6-8, 2-3 inch biscuits

2 cups flour

¼ cup sugar

1 teaspoon baking powder

¼ teaspoon baking soda

½ teaspoon sea salt

⅓ cup shortening

¾ cup buttermilk

Filling

¼ – ⅓ cup fruit preserves, previously mixed with 2-3 tablespoons fresh or freshly frozen and thawed fruit. Store any excess covered in the refrigerator for up to 3 days.

HIGH ALTITUDE TIP

Add 2 extra tablespoons flour and 1 extra tablespoon buttermilk to the batter.

1. Thoroughly Grease a 9-inch round pan with butter or margarine. Prepare the biscuits.

2. Mix the dry ingredients in a large bowl until combined. Cut the shortening into the dry ingredients using two knives, forks, or the paddle on an electric mixer until the ingredients are coarse and crumbly.

3. Gradually add the buttermilk and mix the ingredients together just until they are incorporated. (Do not over beat the dough; instead remove it from the bowl while a few crumbs can still be seen in the bottom of the mixing bowl.)

4. Remove the dough and crumbs from the bowl, place it on a lightly floured surface, and then knead the crumbs into dough. (Do not over-knead the dough, 3-4 times is enough, more can make the biscuits tough and heavy.) Once the crumbs are thoroughly incorporated into the dough, pat the dough out to about 1-1¼ inches thick.

5. Using a 2-3-inch round or shaped cookie cutter or the opening of a glass jar, and cut out individual biscuits.

6. Place each biscuit onto the prepared pan and bake for 14-16 minutes or until golden on top.

7. While the biscuits are baking, gently stir any liquid that has settled on top of the preserves, into the mixture.

8. Lightly spread a smidgen of canola-based butter spread on the top of each biscuit upon removal from the oven.

9. Break the warm biscuits in half, place a dollop of the chunky preserves onto a half of each biscuit and then top each with remaining biscuit half. Wrap each in plastic wrap and store in a freezer-safe bag or airtight plastic container in the freezer.

10. To thaw and serve, remove the plastic wrap, and then wrap each sandwich loosely in a paper towel and microwave on high for about 60 seconds or until warm or hot.

✧ ✧ ✧

✐ BISCUIT VARIATIONS ✐

✧ Add ½ teaspoon cinnamon, ¼ teaspoon nutmeg, ½ cup raisins or finely chopped nuts to the dough prior to mixing.

GREEN EGGS AND HAM

Just in case your little ones squirm at the greenish tint provided by the darker leaves of spinach, remind them that these sandwiches are some of Dr. Seuss's favorites and will help them grow big and strong.

✧

Makes 4 sandwiches

4 English muffins or 8 pieces of whole grain toast

6 large eggs or equivalent amount of liquid egg substitute

¼ cup or more of finely chopped fresh, or freshly frozen spinach

3 scallion bulbs, finely diced

¼ cup milk

Salt and pepper to taste

¼ teaspoon dill

Couple drops of Tabasco® or hot sauce (optional)

4 thin slices of deli-cut ham (optional)

4 ounces of grated Swiss, Munster or marbled Colby cheese

1. Grease a medium size frying pan by adding the small amount of butter or margarine and heat over medium heat.

2. Crack the eggs against the side of a bowl and pour the insides into the bowl.

3. Add the spinach and scallions to the eggs and then mix vigorously while adding the milk and spices until all ingredients are thoroughly incorporated.

4. Pour the egg mixture into the hot frying pan, and with a spatula stir until all the egg mixture begins to solidify; and then sprinkle the cheese on top of the eggs. (The eggs will cook a little more when reheated, so you will want to store them moist, but not runny.)

5. Cover the pan for a few seconds allowing the cheese to slightly melt, and then remove from the pan from the heat.

6. To assemble the sandwiches, first place a piece of ham onto a slice of the bread, then scoop equal amounts of eggs onto the ham slices and top with the remaining bread. Wrap each sandwich individually in plastic wrap; and then store them in freezer-safe bag or an airtight plastic container while still warm to retain moisture. Freeze up to one month.

7. To thaw, unwrap the plastic wrap from around a sandwich and then wrap it loosely in a paper towel to prevent the bread from getting tough in the microwave. Heat the sandwich for 60-90 seconds in the microwave or until hot.

Cheese and Fruit Wraps

It's a common habit for most kids to want a snack late in the afternoon. Often kids prefer snacks that are starchy, salty and/or sweet, and not very nutritious. However, when these snacks are not available, they have to settle for the choices that you do have available. There are endless amounts of awesome tasting snacks that can be easily prepared for satisfying their cravings. This is one of them, not too filling, sweet enough to please, and filled with the goodness of wholesome flavor.

✧

TIP:

❤ *Dates are a great source for increasing energy, removing a body's bacterial waste and for strengthening the heart.*

✧

Serves 3-4

6 thin slices of Munster cheese   12 almonds or walnuts, optional

6 fresh pitted dates

1. Cut each slice of cheese in half crosswise. Cut each date in half lengthwise.

2. Place a nut tightly against the side of each date slice, and then wrap each with a cheese slice. Pinch the edges together to seal, or secure with a toothpick.

3. Serve immediately or place the fruit wraps onto a plate, cover the plate tightly with plastic wrap and place in the refrigerator for later on. For best flavor, serve the same day that these are made.

Orange Muffins

The sun shall shine inside with this magnificent alternative to prepackaged breakfast cakes, bars or doughnuts, especially early in the morning. A scrumptious source of vitamins, these muffins are filled with an irresistible flavor that only a homemade endeavor can provide. Just remember that you love your kids and know that 1 serving of a baked treat per day is enough. So when the times get tough, stay strong and refuse to give into pleas for more.

✧

Preheat oven to 375° Fahrenheit

Makes 6 large or 12 regular sized muffins

6 tangelos, 5-6 small juicing oranges or 3-4 large navel oranges

¾ cup sugar

1 tablespoon orange extract

2 eggs

½ cup canola oil

2 cups plus 2 tablespoons flour

1 teaspoon baking powder

½ teaspoon baking soda

1 inch long twig of orange balsam, finely minced (optional where available)

⅔ cup cranberries, chopped nuts, mini chocolate chips, or blueberries, (optional)

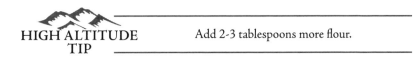

HIGH ALTITUDE TIP   Add 2-3 tablespoons more flour.

1. Wash and cut just the tops and bottoms off of each orange.

2. Cut each orange into sections and using a food processor, process all but 1-2 oranges using the grating wheel. You should have a little over 1 cup. Squeeze the juice from remaining oranges into the measuring cup to a measure of

1½ to 1⅔ cups of grated oranges and juice. You may need to squeeze another half of an orange into the measuring cup, depending on the type and size of the oranges. (I recommend purchasing an extra orange or 2 just in case they are needed. If not needed, know that they won't go to waste, as you or the kids can easily gobble up the excess orange while the muffins bake in the oven.)

3. Thoroughly grease 6 sections of a large muffin pan (or 12 regular sized muffin pan sections) with pan spray, butter or margarine.

4. Thoroughly mix together the eggs, sugar, oranges, oil, and orange extract in a mixing bowl. Add flour, baking powder, baking soda, and orange balsam. Mix all ingredients together until thoroughly incorporated.

5. Using a rubber spatula or large serving spoon, scoop the batter evenly into each prepared muffin section and drizzle the top of each muffin with a small amount of additional juice, if available.

6. Bake large muffins for 25-30 minutes or regular-sized muffins for 15-20 minutes, or until an inserted knife or toothpick comes out clean.

7. Remove all muffins from the pan within a minute or two to prevent further baking. Wrap each individually in plastic wrap. Do not store muffins in a plastic container or they will get too soggy and inedible.

HINTS

- Always mix the ingredients together at low speed and never over beat a muffin or mini-bread batter, as it could affect the product's texture.

- To store muffins for future snacks, place wrapped muffins into freezer-safe bags and freeze accordingly. Thaw naturally or remove the wrapping and thaw on high in the microwave for a minute or 2 or until warm to the touch.

- These make a great alternative snack for after school or late at night

Edamame

This is one of the few recipes in which you can eat many and still not get enough of the flavor. Perfect for quenching the craving for salty snacks between meals, just without the excess fat.

✧

TIP:

> ♥ *Edamame are actually raw soybeans, often referred to a "sweet beans." Each and every individual bean is loaded with energy producing proteins and antioxidants to help fight infections.*

✧

1 pound of fresh edamame pods   ½-1 teaspoon Sea Salt for flavoring

1. In a large saucepan or pot, heat the water above high heat until it reaches a rolling boil.

2. Add the edamame to the boiling water and boil for 7-10 minutes or until tender and you can see a few pods just begin to open.

3. Remove the pan from the heat, thoroughly drain the water, and then run very cold water over the pods until they begin to chill. Drain the pods thoroughly using a colander.

4. Place the edamame in a bowl, sprinkle salt on top and mix it around the pods and then serve or chill until serving.

5. To eat, hold the stem with you fingers and slide the beans out with your other fingers or teeth. Discard the outer pods.

Smoothies and Slushies

Fresh fruits wisely purchased in bulk, then pitted and peeled, and stashed in the freezer for use at another time, not only helps to save funds, but offers the primary ingredient necessary to produce these succulent treats for a quick meal or snack any time of the year. Smoothies, though similar to a milkshake, are primarily made with milk/juice, yogurt, fruits and ice cubes. Slushies, on the other hand, are prepared with ice cubes, juice and fruits. Fortunately both are fun and tasty, and once you show the older kids how to make these, they can make them for themselves. Also, keep in mind that older kids will likely have a larger glassful than their little, younger siblings.

✧

BANARAMA SMOOTHIES

Flavors can vary according to personal tastes.

✧

Serves 2-4

HINTS

🎀 To thicken the smoothie, use less juice or milk.

🎀 It is best to use bananas before they begin to brown to ensure maximum flavor.

2 medium bananas

2 cups berries, chopped fresh pineapple, papayas, mangos, or peeled and sliced apples

1½ cups plain yogurt

2 cups 100% pineapple, orange, grapefruit, or apple juice

2 tablespoons honey or sugar

2-3 cups ice or Fruity Cubes (page 63)

1. Mix all ingredients thoroughly in a blender until smooth.

2. Divide the mixture between 2-4 glasses and serve with a straw.

POM CHERIE SMOOTHIE

✧

TIP:

♥ *Pomegranates, an ancient symbol of love, are one of Mother Nature's finest creations. While the fruit and juice may appear pricey, please know that rewards to your health will be bountiful.*

✧

Serves 2

1½ cups 100% pomegranate juice

2 cups pitted sweet dark cherries

2 cups plain yogurt

¼ teaspoon pure almond or vanilla extract

2 tablespoons honey or sugar

2-3 cups ice or Fruity Cubes (page 63)

1. Mix all ingredients thoroughly in a blender until smooth.
2. Divide the mixture between 2 tall glasses and serve with a straw.

PEACHY THICK AND CRUNCHY SMOOTHIE

✧

Serves 2-4

---

1 cup milk

2½ cups Vanilla yogurt

2 fresh peaches, peeled and sliced or 2 cups previously frozen peaches, thawed

¼ cup pecan pieces

2 dashes ginger powder or ¼ teaspoon finely minced fresh ginger

2-3 cups ice or Fruity Cubes (page 63)

1. Thoroughly mix the milk/juice, yogurt, vanilla, ice cubes and peaches in a blender until smooth.

2. Gently break the nuts into pieces, and then fold them into the mixture with a spoon prior to serving.

3. Divide the smoothie between 2-4 glasses and serve.

HINTS

- 🌸 To easily peel peaches, blanch them in boiling water for 4-6 minutes and then peel away the outer skin.

- 🌸 If using previously frozen and thawed peaches, eliminate ¼ cup of the milk and add the peach juice after thawing to the mixture instead.

- 🌸 Peaches being one of Mother Nature's sweetest natural foods, eliminates the need to add sugar or honey to this recipe.

The Slushies

Perfect to serve as a snack, especially on warmer days. It is best to use fresh fruits and juices to gain the most flavor and slush. The varieties of citrus fruits stored in cans and jars may have sweetener added to maximize shelf life and flavor.

✧

A TANG OF SLUSH

Serves 2

4 grapefruits or 5 large oranges

Juice of 2 lemons

Juice of 2 limes or 1 orange

2-3 cups Fruity Cubes made with whole berries (page 63)

2 teaspoons honey or sugar

1. Peel and segment the grapefruits or oranges into a bowl.
2. Mix the lemon and lime juice with the fruit and freeze for an hour or more.
3. Remove the bowl from the freezer and pour the fruit into a blender.
4. Add the Fruity Cubes (page 63) to the fruit and blend for about 30 seconds until the fruit and cubes are crushed and all of the ingredients are slushy.
5. Pour the contents from the blender into glasses and serve with a straw.

HINT

🍒 You can always use a combination of 1¼ cup 100% grapefruit juice and about 1 cup of 100% orange juice instead of the fruit.

BEAT THE BLUES SLUSHIE

A favorite treat to beat the blues!

TIP:

♥ *Remember that Blueberries are filled with nutrients that help heal our bodies, while promoting the ability to focus and pay attention, thus the more they are served, the better.*

Serves 2

---

2 cups blueberries

2 cups unsweetened pineapple juice

2 bananas, each sliced into 3 pieces

2 teaspoons honey

2-3 cups Fruity Cubes (page 63)

1. Mix the fruits and juice into a bowl and freeze for an hour or more.
2. Put the frozen juice, fruits and Fruity Cubes into a blender and blend for about 30 seconds until all ingredients are crushed and slushy.
3. Divide the contents in the blender between 2 glasses and serve with a straw.

✧

MELLOW MELON SLUSHIE

Serves 2-3

½ seedless watermelon, cantaloupe, honeydew, papaya or mango chopped into 1-inch pieces

8 strawberries, stemmed and preferably hulled

3 cups Fruity Cubes (page 63)

1. Place fruits and Fruity Cubes into a blender and blend for about 20-30 seconds until all ingredients are crushed and slushy.
2. Divide the Slushie between 2-3 glasses and serve with a straw.

Yeastless Rolls of Cinn

Have you ever seen your kids' eyes light up with joy when they see fresh cinnamon rolls, especially those that ooze with globs of icing? Yes, Cinnamon rolls are rolls of delectable joy for many, but most varieties are loaded with excess icing, fats and sugars, thus not a good choice when trying to maintain a healthy body weight, lose weight or prevent excess weight gains. Yet, for many they are a favorite, and on a special occasion the serving of one per person is fine; it is just the preferred choice that needs to change. Therefore I provide you with a personal favorite, which only takes a few minutes to prepare and then bake, and is guaranteed to fill your home with the sweet fragrance of homemade love.

✧

TIP:

♥ *Cinnamon is a favorite ancient spice that comes from the inner bark of small, leafy Evergreen trees, primarily found in Sri Lanka and the southern parts of India. Natural, fragrant, spicy and sweet; cinnamon is filled with healing properties that help to alleviate stomachaches, indigestion and nausea. Also, recent studies have been found that it can also help control type 2 Diabetes, improve energy levels and assist in blood circulation.*

✧

Preheat oven to 400° Fahrenheit	Makes 6 cinnamon rolls

2 cups flour	½ teaspoon sea salt
¼ cup sugar	⅔ cup brown sugar
1 teaspoon baking powder	⅓ cup shortening
¼ teaspoon baking soda	1 tablespoon cinnamon
¾ cup buttermilk	⅔ cup raisins or craisins
3 tablespoons canola-based butter spread	

HIGH ALTITUDE
TIP

Add 2 extra tablespoons flour and
1 extra tablespoon buttermilk to the batter.

1. Completely cover the bottom and sides of a 9x9-inch pan with butter or margarine.

2. Mix the dry ingredients in a large bowl until combined.

3. Cut the shortening into the dry ingredients using two knives, forks, or the paddle on an electric mixer until the ingredients are coarse and crumbly.

4. Gradually add the buttermilk and mix these ingredients together just until they are incorporated. (Do not over beat the dough; instead remove it from the bowl while a few crumbs can still be seen in the bottom of the mixing bowl.)

5. Remove the dough and crumbs from the bowl, place it on a lightly floured surface and gently knead the crumbs into the dough (about 3-4 kneads). Once the crumbs are thoroughly incorporated into the dough, pat and roll the dough out into a rectangle about 12x8-inches wide and until the dough is about ¼-inch thick.

HINT

I admit Cinnamon Rolls are my very favorite baked treat. I can actually tell how good a bakery's products are just by looking at their Cinnamon Rolls. Therefore, please trust that although these are very easy to make, the flavor is phenomenal!

6. Spread the canola-based spread all over the dough. Sprinkle the raisins all over the top of the canola-based butter spread, then sprinkle the brown sugar on top of the raisins, breaking up any lumps as you go, and then evenly sprinkle the cinnamon on top of the brown sugar.

7. Beginning at the longest edge, roll the dough up tightly like a jellyroll, tucking the sides in as you go. Pinch the edge tightly into the dough to seal the ingredients in, and then slice the roll crosswise, into 6 equal pieces.

8. Place each piece into the prepared pan, cut side down and bake for approximately 14-18 minutes or until golden.

9. Remove the pan from the oven, spread a little bit of the canola spread all over the top and sides of each roll and serve hot for best flavor. Store them covered in plastic wrap or in a tightly fitted plastic container for up to 2 days.

Merry Berry Bars

Not everyone is hungry first thing in the morning, but as a good parent you know that your family members need something to eat to awaken their minds and bodies; while preventing snacking on junk foods prior to lunch. So what do you do; toss them prepackaged fix as they run out the door or hand them one of these delicious bars, loaded with brainpower from the berries tucked within. Although the choice is yours, remember that their quality of life and health is in your hands, not those of a manufacturer.

✦

TIP:

💜 *When making better food decisions for your family, one of the best changes you can make is to use canola oil in your recipes; rather than vegetable or corn. Canola oil contains the lowest amount of saturated fats of all cooking oils, has a nice light flavor and helps to promote a healthy heart. Additionally, in a diverse range of recipes, canola oil is a healthy substitute for melted butter or margarine, and canola-based butter spreads offer a satisfying flavor, while reducing the amount of fat, cholesterol and calories in a variety of recipes.*

✦

Preheat oven to 350° Fahrenheit

¾ cup canola oil

3 cups oats

2¼ cups flour

¾ cup brown sugar or brown sugar substitute

1½ teaspoons cinnamon

4 cups blueberries, fresh or frozen

2 cups raspberries, fresh or frozen

1½ tablespoons flour

½ cup raspberry preserves (sugar-free preserves are fine)

1. Mix the margarine, oats, 2¼ cups flour, sugar and cinnamon until ingredients begin to hold together, leaving some crumbs on the bottom of the bowl. The dough will be somewhat moist.

2. Thoroughly grease a 9x13-inch pan with unflavored pan spray.

3. Gather most of the moistest batter with your fingers and then evenly press them into the prepared pan. Take more batter from the bowl as you go to thoroughly cover the bottom of the pan. Keep approximately 1 cup of crumbs in the mixing bowl.

4. Bake the bottom crust for 15-20 minutes.

5. While baking the crust, prepare the filling:

Filling:

6. In a medium bowl, place the blueberries, raspberries, preserves and 1½ tablespoons of flour. Gently mix all ingredients with a spoon or rubber spatula until the preserves are thoroughly incorporated with the fruits.

7. Remove the crust from the oven and then using a rubber spatula, immediately spread the filling evenly, completely covering the crust.

8. Remix the reserved crumbs once again to further break them up, and then sprinkle the crumbs all over the filling.

9. Bake the bars for another 20 minutes. Allow the bars to cool completely before cutting.

10. Once cool, cut the bars into 12 pieces, remove each piece and individually wrap in plastic wrap. They can be stored as they are for up to 3 days or placed in a freezer-safe bag and frozen. To thaw frozen bars, simply unwrap each bar and microwave for about a minute or until thawed and warm. They can be enjoyed right then, or rewrapped and enjoyed later in the morning, such as on the bus or in-between classes.

No More Overflowing Plates Just for One

One of the hardest parts of making better food decisions and modeling healthful eating habits is controlling the amounts of food some of the male family members eat. I don't know about your household, but in mine the men always seemed to get the largest bowl of soup, piece of meat, or serving of pasta.

Unfortunately, this ritual can often be passed onto kids who wish to be "just like dad." You know that it is always best for parents to agree on all decisions that affect your children, but occasionally a little reminder may be necessary for the sake of the children.

During these times, remind your husband that over-sizing his servings will be ceased in favor of more salads and fruits in his diet. If he starts to complain, whine or argue, simply remind him as you would the kids, *"I am sorry honey, but we made these decisions together and you know that these changes are because I love you all and want all of us to eat better so that we and the kids have lots more energy to enjoy life with."*

Losing by Moving

E arlier, I mentioned that overeating and poor food choices are not the only causes of excessive weight gain; lack of exercise is another cause that needs to be addressed. It is a proven fact that exercise helps each of us to maintain a healthy weight; and children especially need some kind of vigorous daily physical activity for their bodies to grow and develop healthfully. In fact research has shown *"that lack of vigorous physical activity is the main contributor of obesity for adolescents between 11 and 15 years of age"* (Medical News Today). Besides, exercise helps your kids to sleep better, and prepare their brains for the next days tasks.

Many of you already know that your child is overweight and are consciously making better food choices. (Way to go mom and dad!) But in today's busy world, finding extra time to play, go for walks, ride bikes or swim with your kids can be difficult.

You know that your kids need more exercise, but what can you do when you are not always home and they prefer to do nothing but watch television, or sit in front of a computer exercising his/her thumbs playing video games for hours? No problem! You can always set up a plan with your school's physical education teacher or the local YMCA or recreation center. Often there are training classes before and/or after school, as well as on weekends, for various activities. Your child can participate in these activities either as a helper or as an active participant. Just because a child may not be very athletic, does not mean that they cannot be good helpers! Over time, he or she will become accepted as a member of the group, and new friendships will also likely be established, encouraging them to continue in the activity. A better self-image will also likely develop as that excess weight begins to drop.

Getting your kids more physically active can involve so much more than just playing sports. They can always get out and shovel snow, mow a neighbor's lawn, play jump rope or even walk an elderly neighbor's dog. There are many activities that your children can do inside too, especially if the weather or neighborhood is bad. Video games that produce movement, whereby the player has to physically maneuver the screen players to participate in the game, provides a fun source of exercise. Or how about dancing? Kids naturally love music and there are many songs and video games that promote dancing. Overall, it doesn't matter what type of activity they engage in, as long as they do something that gets them actively moving their bodies; rather than sitting around, doing nothing, but watching TV, or exercising their thumbs while playing sedentary video games.

Another great option is to encourage and teach them how to dig and grow a garden. Even just a little spot of grass or dirt can be converted to a small, but pretty garden. True, many inner city neighborhoods do not have space for a garden, especially if you live in an apartment. However, there are many flowers and herbs that can easily be grown on a windowsill or even a small balcony in small containers. Initially, some children might not be very enthused about helping carry the necessary equipment, and then digging in the dirt. Oh, but just watch their faces shine with excitement when those first little sprouts of green begin to pop up through the soil. Plus, if space allows, they can plant various veggies and fruits, to be harvested and prepared into naturally grown, homemade, edible delights. Their physical efforts of digging, watering and weeding, and then watching those little green sprouts grow into flowers, fragrant herbs and/or a small crop of veggies and fruits produces positive feelings of accomplishment and joy, while building self-confidence. But, their work has not yet ended for they must also harvest and prune their plants once grown. Overall gardening is a terrific way to get them out of the chair and moving while toning their bodies, as they prepare a cornucopia of rich colors, flavors and scents.

Setting rules with your kid's input, whereby they agree to actively play for an hour or more before that movie, favorite television show or video game gets turned on is another option. Know that kids are more likely to follow and respect rules and associated consequences (such as losing the privilege to watch TV or use the computer for a designated period of time), when they partake in the setting of new rules and consequences. Thus, if or when challenged, it is easier to remind then that they were actually the ones who came up with the associated consequences! Additionally, know that when they attempt to challenge these rules, you are then given a choice. Either feed into their negativity, ensuring unwanted stress and aggravation, or offer a patient smile while reminding them that this was their choice to make, not yours. And then remember to smile and remind them *"these rules were made so that they have more energy to play and enjoy life with!"*

Lastly, remember that you are their primary role model. Therefore, if you tend to sit around doing nothing all day, you must begin to get more active as well. So get up and get your body moving too. You can always dance or jump rope with your kids, have them teach you how to play those video games that produce movement, take them for a walk around your favorite park or nature center, or even walk around the local mall. Plus playing outside with your kids provides a natural dose of Vitamin D, offered from the sun shining down upon you. A little bit of effort on your part goes a long way. You'll actually find that just spending some active time laughing with and simply enjoying your kids is more fun than you thought. Besides, kids are only young for a short period of time, so enjoy their company while they are still children.

ADD MORE
FRUITS & VEGETABLES

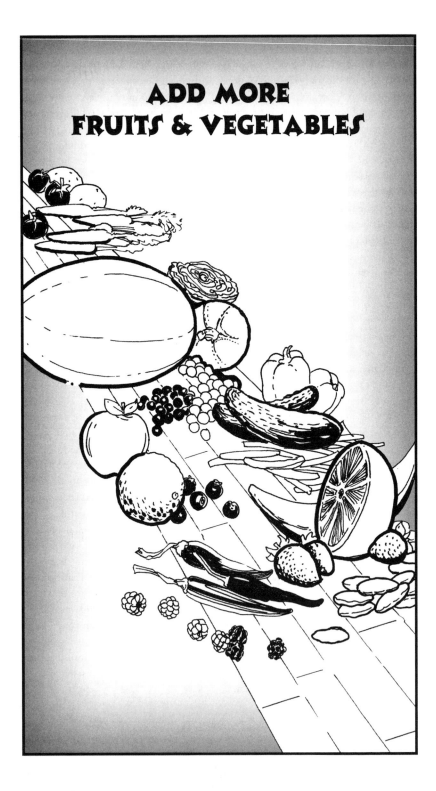

How to Add More Fruits and Vegetables into Your Food Selections

Most people, especially children, do not consume enough fruits and vegetables on a daily basis. As a parent, you know that your kids need to eat more of these foods, but often wonder just how to manage that, especially with fussy eaters. You purchase fresh fruits and veggies, but a few days later, they have begun to get mushy, have sprouted some form of fuzzy growth, or have simply turned brown beyond recognition. So, once again, they get tossed into the trash bin. What a waste!

If only you had chosen to use those fruits and veggies in various foods, snacks and treats, they could have been saved and savored. There are many ways to add a smidgen of this and some of that to foods to make them healthier without making them less palatable. Several of the recipes within these pages are supplied for this purpose. In the meantime, consider these suggestions and get creative when making better food decisions for your children. Also, remember that when introducing a new food, including fruits or veggies to your family, to describe it as fun and tasty, rather than healthy and good for them. Fun and tasty is a more positive approach, and will help your kids to develop better eating habits that will last a lifetime.

Additionally, do not force your child to eat. They may not be hungry or may honestly not like the dish served. Instead of punishing or forcing them to eat, be proactive and give them options of fruits, yogurt or salad instead. It has been found that eating more fruits helps to control unwanted weight gains in children and adults. Plus, fruits can fill and satisfy hunger pangs and are a much more positive choice than punishing your child for not eating or for disliking the food offered

TIP:

 For simple reference purposes, the primary difference between fruits and vegetables is that fruits contain seeds, while veggies do not. However, because many fruits provide a pungent, savory flavor instead of sweet flavor, some are placed in the vegetable aisles at the grocery store. Additionally, beans, nuts and many whole grains are also considered a fruit.

✧

HINTS

Just in case you happen to reside in what has been referred to as 'Produce Deserts' (*Denver Post*, 2010), which is a neighborhood or group of neighborhoods that lack access to fresh produce, there are suggestions for overcoming this situation listed in the last chapter of this book (page 205).

- Fruits can be added to so many foods, not just those made for snacks and desserts. Marinating a piece of beef, pork or poultry in spices and 100 percent fruit juice or fruit (i.e. cherry, pomegranate, cranberry, orange, lemon or peach) adds wonderful flavor.

- Raisins, apples, peaches and/or apricots in addition to the breadcrumbs, diced celery, and onions superbly complement dressings and stuffing. And adding just a handful of chopped nuts into stuffing or salad recipes adds a marvelous, crunchy flavor to the final product.

- Add a small amount (1-2 tablespoons per person) of finely minced spinach to foods such as tomato-based sauces, macaroni and cheese, potato/pasta salad, scrambled eggs, pizza, meatloaf, etc.

- Adding fresh or freshly frozen fruits to items such as pancake or waffle batter offers a naturally sweet flavor, and may decrease the desire for excess syrup.

- Add a few chopped grapes or dried fruits to egg salad, chicken salad, or even a pot pie. Also, a handful of chopped nuts or seeds (walnuts, pecans, almonds, and sunflower or pumpkin seeds) will enhance the flavor of numerous foods.

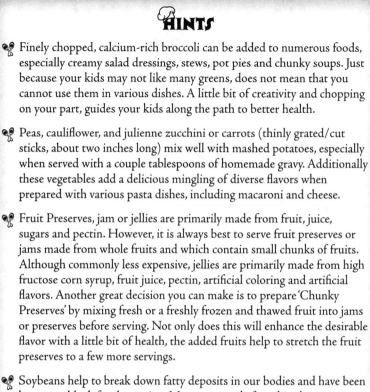

HINTS

- Finely chopped, calcium-rich broccoli can be added to numerous foods, especially creamy salad dressings, stews, pot pies and chunky soups. Just because your kids may not like many greens, does not mean that you cannot use them in various dishes. A little bit of creativity and chopping on your part, guides your kids along the path to better health.

- Peas, cauliflower, and julienne zucchini or carrots (thinly grated/cut sticks, about two inches long) mix well with mashed potatoes, especially when served with a couple tablespoons of homemade gravy. Additionally these vegetables add a delicious mingling of diverse flavors when prepared with various pasta dishes, including macaroni and cheese.

- Fruit Preserves, jam or jellies are primarily made from fruit, juice, sugars and pectin. However, it is always best to serve fruit preserves or jams made from whole fruits and which contain small chunks of fruits. Although commonly less expensive, jellies are primarily made from high fructose corn syrup, fruit juice, pectin, artificial coloring and artificial flavors. Another great decision you can make is to prepare 'Chunky Preserves' by mixing fresh or a freshly frozen and thawed fruit into jams or preserves before serving. Not only does this will enhance the desirable flavor with a little bit of health, the added fruits help to stretch the fruit preserves to a few more servings.

- Soybeans help to break down fatty deposits in our bodies and have been known to block fat absorption. Most commonly found in the grocery as edamame, these sweet, softened soybeans in the pod; can be added to many foods, especially soups, chilies, burritos, and various salads. They are also super to snack on in-between meals.

Healthier Foods
Do Not Need To Be Expensive

M any may resist making better food decisions or be hesitant when making their purchases because of cost. Always keep in mind that there are many things in life you can cut back on, but you should never, ever, cut back on fresh food for those you love or who are placed in your care. You can cut back on funds spent on clothes, shoes, cleaning supplies, DVDs and various extras that help make your days brighter. But fresh and freshly frozen food supplies nutrition and life to our bodies. It helps us to think better, grow stronger, and ultimately live longer. So why would you want to cut back on such an important ingredient of life?

Making healthful food decisions does not need to be expensive; often it is just a matter of choice. Yes, those prepackaged foods are tempting, but why waste your hard earned funds primarily paying for a manufacturer's packaging materials, when you can make flavorful, homemade versions of the same food. Grocery store aisles are filled with frozen and quick to prepare foods, as well as sugar and fat saturated snacks. Sure, these foods are made to help make your life easier; but remember that much of their price primarily comes from the packaging, not the actual food inside. Homemade varieties of these same foods will actually cost you the same or less in the long run, are easy to prepare, and will likely taste much better. Additionally, purchasing some foods simply for price and ease (super-sized bags of prepackaged foods and snacks) could eventually cost you more in time and money spent on doctors and medications resulting from too much of a bad thing.

Another issue to consider when making better food choices is that food shopping does take dedication and time to read the labels before tossing various products into your cart. For instance when you're reading the list of ingredients on a product and you see "High Fructose Corn Syrup and/or Trans Fats" listed, then you know that this item is not beneficial to your family's health. When you encounter this, immediately put the product back on the shelf before the temptation of ease surfaces. Also, consider that many of the same types of products (yogurts, sour cream, crackers, sauces, etc.) have different amounts of sugar and salt listed, and you will want to purchase those items with the least amount of each.

Another easy choice is related to purchasing canned fruits. Avoid purchasing those stored in heavy syrup. All they supply is an overdose of sugar that causes a sugar rush, poor concentration and potential behavior problems once the rush begins to crash. Yet, if you must purchase canned fruits, pick those stored in juice or water instead. They will not cost you more, and your children will be much more enjoyable to be around.

Because the cost of food is continually rising, I suggest that you use this fact to your advantage when making better food choices for your family. For instance, purchasing fruits and veggies in bulk during the warmer months will help save funds during the chilly months and is not as time consuming as you may think. Many varieties of fresh summer fruits and veggies can be grown in a home garden, purchased at a farmer's market or bought on sale at the grocery store, then quickly washed, pitted and chopped to be stored in the freezer for use at another time (see page 206 for details). Also, stock up during sales on items such as flour, sugar, rice, beans, spices, herbs, and dried fruits and nuts, as well as meats, fish, and poultry that can be frozen. Bulk suppliers are great places to stock up on whole grain cereals, dairy products, paper goods, canned veggies and fruits, and cooking oils such as canola oil. It's all about picking and choosing the foods that provide nourishment and good flavor, rather than picking foods based simply on ease and price.

Feel Better Tea

An unavoidable part of being a parent is dealing with common childhood illnesses such as runny noses, stomachaches, headaches, or whatever else may momentarily ail your children. So what can you do to help them feel better sooner rather than later? You prepare a soothing beverage that helps to relieve the symptoms of these common ailments, while waiting for the doctor to call you back. Although not a cure, this lovely tea does help the kids (and adults) to feel better and is much more beneficial to the body than a sugar-laden soda.

✧

TIP:

♥ *Ginger is a natural spice that helps to alleviate numerous bodily ailments, such as nausea, stomachaches, indigestion, gas, fevers and colds, headaches and possibly bad cholesterol. In addition, combining both ginger and honey in various foods and beverages has been found to decrease the symptoms of respiratory ailments, such as congestion, coughs, and sore throats.*

✧

5 thin slices raw ginger	2 teaspoons honey
3 cups water	2 teaspoons fresh lemon juice

1. Peel a small portion of the Ginger Root to expose its inner layer, with a knife or vegetable peeler.

2. Cut 5 very thin slices of ginger into a saucepan and add the water.

3. Boil the water for 15-20 minutes for maximum flavor and medicinal benefits.

4. Drain the water into a cup with a sieve and discard the ginger slices.

5. Mix the lemon juice and honey into the cup and serve.

HINT

🌿 To store the ginger root, you can wrap it in plastic wrap or seal it in a freezer-safe baggie and place it in the refrigerator or freezer for use at another time.

Homemade Oatmeal

Research has found that although conveniently easy, those small packages of instant oatmeal contain more sugar than necessary, and many contain artificial flavorings. Plus they can be a tad more expensive than homemade varieties. Making your own is just as easy, less expensive, and you get to control the amount of sugar added.

TIPS:

- ♥ *Oatmeal is filled with natural fiber and protein, and helps to lower cholesterol levels, helps to reduce the risk of heart disease and may reduce the risk for developing Type 2 Diabetes.*

- ♥ *Cinnamon has been found to be a natural sweetener, as well as a resource for helping prevent Type 2 Diabetes.*

- ♥ *A recent study conducted by Boston's Children's Hospital found that kids who <u>only</u> ate instant oatmeal for breakfast had an increased appetite throughout the day, resulting in the consumption of more food. While instant varieties appear easier, homemade is just as easy to prepare in about the same amount of time. Plus, homemade oatmeal has been known to help eliminate the desire to eat before the next meal, especially when served with a sprinkling of fresh or dried fruit on top.*

- ♥ *Non-sweetened Oatmeal can also be used to heal acne. All you need to do is prepare an average serving size with water, allow it to cool until warm and apply it to the affected areas. Let the oatmeal set on the affected area for a few minutes and then rinse it off. Repeat twice a day until the acne is healed. Store any leftovers, covered in the refrigerator for use the next day. Oatmeal also helps to moisturize and soften our skin.*

Makes 1 serving

½ cup quick or old-fashioned oats

½ cup water

½ cup milk

1 teaspoons sugar, brown sugar, honey or sugar substitute

1-2 tablespoons dried, fresh or freshly frozen and thawed fruits (raisins, blueberries, sweet dark pitted cherries, ½ banana sliced, etc.

¼ (or less) teaspoon cinnamon

Mix all ingredients into a single serving bowl and microwave on high for approximately 2 minutes. Allow the cereal to set in the microwave for about 30 seconds, remove, stir, and serve.

✧ ✧ ✧

✐ VARIATIONS ✐

✧ Add ½ teaspoon of maple extract for maple flavor, especially if using peeled and diced apples.

✧ Eliminate the added sugar and swirl 2 teaspoons of chunky preserves into each serving after the cereal has been cooked.

HINTS

❧ Withhold the bananas or blueberries until after the oatmeal is prepared, and then mix these fruits into the cereal and serve.

❧ For a thinner version, add an extra tablespoon or two of water.

❧ This recipe can be doubled, tripled or more.

Ooey Gooey Grilled Cheese with Pizzazz

Easy, pleasing, and inexpensive, what more could you ask for?
(Well, maybe a hot bowl of tomato soup on the side.)

✧

TIP:

♥ *Cheeses that have been prepared naturally from whole milk are much more beneficial to your child's health than soft, processed varieties. Soft, processed cheese and cheese spreads may be prepared with excess fats to ensure a longer shelf life.*

✧

Makes 2 open-faced sandwiches

2 slices wheat, cinnamon raisin, whole grain, or rye bread

2 slices cheese, e.g. Cheddar, Swiss, Munster, Jarlsberg, Monterey Jack, Marbled Colby, or Havarti

4 tablespoons blueberries, raisins, chopped dried apricots, sliced strawberries, halved cherries, diced apples, sliced grapes.

1-2 teaspoons chopped nuts or seeds, such as walnuts, pecans, pumpkin or sunflower seeds (optional)

Canola or olive oil based butter spread

1. Lightly spread one side of each piece of bread lightly with a small amount of canola-based butter spread and place this side down into medium sized frying pan.

2. Sprinkle the fruits and/or nuts evenly onto the bread slices and then top each with a slice of cheese. Or for younger children, you can add the fruit and/or nuts on top of the cheese in a pattern (smiley face, flower, geometric design, etc.).

3. Turn the heat under the frying pan to medium low, add the prepared bread slices and then cover the pan to assist the cheese in melting. Grill the sandwiches for 2-3 minutes, or until the bottom of the bread is golden or browned to taste.

HINTS

- Grilled cheese is a type of sandwich, thus refrain from serving it as a snack between meals; especially when inducing weight loss or preventing excess weight gain.

- If adding dried fruit (raisins, craisins, cherries, apricots) always soak them in very hot--boiling water for about 10 minutes, then drain and pat dry, before adding to any food. This ensures that they are plump and juicy. Hard and dried out fruits can be difficult to chew and taste nasty; hence preventing the kids from enjoying their flavor and gaining the nutritional benefits from these little natural delights.

Oodles of Noodles and Zuchles
(Zucchini Pasta)

Have you ever noticed that after serving canned or boxed pasta and sauce that your kids are hungry again about an hour later? That's because some (though not all) of these prepackaged foods may have excess sugar and salt added for purposes of maximizing taste and shelf life. Additionally, because some these products are relatively low in nutrients, a person's body will want more food shortly after the meal is completed to sustain itself until the next meal.

✧

TIPS:

 Parmesan cheese, as well as other hard cheeses (e.g. Romano), have minimal fat in their make-up which explains why they are so very hard and preferred grated rather than sliced. These cheeses are also full of calcium, which helps to maintain healthy teeth and bones. Therefore, an extra little sprinkle or 2 on top of some food is fine for enhancing the flavor.

 A block of cheese is usually less expensive than those varieties previously sliced or grated.

✧

Preheat oven to 350° F	Serve 6-8

2 tablespoons combined butter and canola or olive oil butter spread

3 medium-large zucchinis

3 cups of your favorite homemade or bottled sauce Tomato Sauce, (see page 20)

1-2 teaspoons of minced garlic (if using canned sauces)

6-8 ounces thinly sliced or grated Provolone and/or Mozzarella Cheese

2 tablespoons Parmesan and/or Romano Cheese

12-ounces package Rotini or Penne pasta

1. Spread the canola-based spread all over the bottom and sides of a 9x13-inch pan.

2. Slice the zucchini into ¼ inch slices and layer all over the pan. Pour the sauce over the zucchini, and then very gently mix the garlic only into the sauce. Bake for 25-30 minutes.

3. Prepare the pasta, according to the package directions.

4. Remove the pan from the oven and cover the entire top with the cheese. Return the pan to the oven and continue baking until the cheese has melted and begins to bubble, about 5-10 minutes.

5. Serve over the warm pasta.

Razzle Dazzle Chicken

One of the biggest excuses for not cooking more meals, and relying on fast or prepackaged food to feed a family with, is that often the parent/caretaker cannot think of a meal to prepare in a minimal amount of time, at minimal cost. Yet there is no need for such excuses, for when you purchase foods wisely, for you can usually prepare a healthful, homemade meal in about the same amount of time it takes to reheat a prepared or prepackaged meal. This recipe is a prime example! Yes, it takes a little bit of effort, but once you mingle freshly frozen and thawed chicken pieces with a bit of fruit, you know that you are offering your family a nutritional meal, filled with spectacular flavor, rather than just some food to quench their hunger with.

✧

Serves 4-6 (depending on age)

1 tablespoon canola or safflower oil

½ cup red onion, chopped

½ teaspoon thyme

½ teaspoon sea salt, divided

4 skinless, boneless chicken breasts (these can be cut in half for little ones)

⅓ cup raspberry preserves, preferably seedless

2 tbsp. apple cider or red wine vinegar (for younger kids, use apple cider)

¼ teaspoon black pepper

Pinch of garlic

½ cup or more fresh raspberries

HINT

The addition of fresh fruits to a plain old everyday meal, such as chicken, can turn the meal into one of scrumptious delight that will be requested again!

1. Heat the oil in a large skillet over medium-high heat. Add the onion to the pan and sauté for about 5 minutes.

2. Sprinkle the thyme and ¼ tsp. salt all over the chicken. Add the chicken to the onions and sauté 6-8 minutes on each side or until easily pierced and juices run clear. Remove the chicken from pan and place it on a plate. Keep it warm by wrapping or covering in tin foil.

3. Reduce the heat under the same pan to medium, and add the remaining salt, preserves, vinegar and pepper to pan. Stir this sauce constantly until preserves melt. Then, divide the chicken pieces between individual plates, spoon the sauce over the chicken, and top each serving with a tablespoon or so of raspberries. Serve this dish immediately with potatoes, wild rice or a green leafy salad.

✧ ✧ ✧

✑ VARIATION ✑

✧ Apricot preserves and diced apples also work well with this recipe, as does peach preserves and diced peaches. If using either variation, add a ¼ teaspoon of nutmeg into pan with the other ingredients.

Loaf of Beef

Wow, what a great alternative to fast food! The cost to feed your family a full meal, not only produces leftovers for a lunch or two later in the week, but the price is equivalent to feeding only 2-3 at a fast food chain. Thus how could you deny your kids such a delicious act of love? Heavenly Mashed Potatoes are splendid to complement to this dish with, as well as some frozen peas. What a great means to save hard earned cash and feed your children healthier food choices. Way to go mom and dad, you rock!

✧

Preheat oven to 350° Fahrenheit

1¼ pounds ground beef

¾ cup plus 2 tablespoons milk

¼ cup ketchup

2 eggs, beaten

⅔ cup bread crumbs (unseasoned)

⅓ cup finely diced onion

½ teaspoon minced garlic

¼ teaspoon each salt, pepper

½ cup ketchup

¼ cup brown sugar (loosely packed)

¼ cup water

1 teaspoon salt (or less)

HINT

🌿 Frozen veggies are fine to purchase and use, especially as a side dish to a meal. However, avoid purchasing the varieties premixed with added salt, butters or sauces, as most are saturated in such, and may contribute to excess weight gain. Adding your own butter or sauce allows you to control the amount of these condiments added, as well as the cost.

1. Place the bread crumbs into a large mixing bowl or bowl.

2. Mix together the milk and ketchup and pour this mixture over the bread crumbs. Allow the crumbs to soak up the milk, and then add the ground beef, eggs, onions, garlic, salt, and pepper to the milk mixture, and mix it all up with your hands or in an electric mixer.

3. Thoroughly grease a 9x5-inch loaf pan well with pan spray, butter, or margarine

4. Gather the meat mixture, shape it into a loaf and then place into the prepared pan.

5. Thoroughly mix together the remaining ketchup, brown sugar, water and salt and pour all over the top of the beef loaf.

6. Bake for approximately 1 hour and 10 minutes. Then remove it from the oven; and gently remove the loaf from the pan using 2 large spatulas. Pour all remaining juice on top, and serve.

Heavenly Mashed Potatoes

Mashed potatoes are a favorite among many, especially children. Unfortunately, most kids have a tendency to scoop too much into their growing bodies when a steaming plate, piled high with comforting, edible bliss, is placed in front of them. Thus, to develop better eating habits in your household, avoid bringing this tempting favorite to the table, and fill the plates individually instead. Most importantly, know that substituting a cupful or more of well-cooked cauliflower for a potato or two is a splendid way to get more veggies into your kids diet; as well as reduce the starch intake from this luscious, comforting favorite.

✧

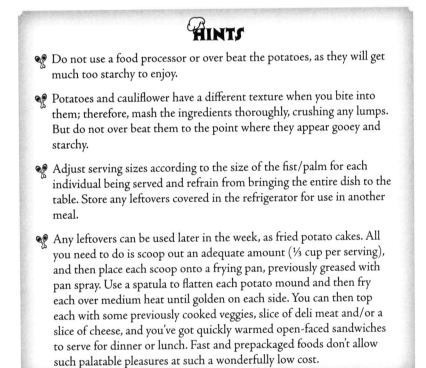

HINTS

- Do not use a food processor or over beat the potatoes, as they will get much too starchy to enjoy.

- Potatoes and cauliflower have a different texture when you bite into them; therefore, mash the ingredients thoroughly, crushing any lumps. But do not over beat them to the point where they appear gooey and starchy.

- Adjust serving sizes according to the size of the fist/palm for each individual being served and refrain from bringing the entire dish to the table. Store any leftovers covered in the refrigerator for use in another meal.

- Any leftovers can be used later in the week, as fried potato cakes. All you need to do is scoop out an adequate amount (⅓ cup per serving), and then place each scoop onto a frying pan, previously greased with pan spray. Use a spatula to flatten each potato mound and then fry each over medium heat until golden on each side. You can then top each with some previously cooked veggies, slice of deli meat and/or a slice of cheese, and you've got quickly warmed open-faced sandwiches to serve for dinner or lunch. Fast and prepackaged foods don't allow such palatable pleasures at such a wonderfully low cost.

TIP:

💜 *Leaving the skin on the potatoes adds more vitamins to the product.*

✦

Serves 4-5

---

3 medium sized potatoes	¼-⅓ cup milk
Enough warm water to cover the potatoes, plus a little more	¼ cup (4 tablespoons or ½ stick) butter, margarine or canola-based spread
1 cup or more of freshly chopped cauliflower florets	Salt and pepper to taste

1. Wash the potatoes completely under warm water. (I normally leave the skin on, but to peel or not, is of personal preference.) Slice potatoes into ¼-inch slices and place into a large pot. Cover with water and boil until tender and soft or about 25 minutes.

2. Place the cauliflower into a microwave-safe bowl, cover with water and microwave on high for 6-10 minutes or until soft and mushy. Thoroughly drain all the water from the vegetable and set aside.

3. Drain and rinse the potatoes under hot water, then pour them into a large bowl.

4. Add the cauliflower, milk, butter/margarine and seasonings and mash with an old-fashioned potato masher or an electric hand mixer until smooth and fluffy and serve.

Oodles of Shrimpy Noodles

❧

Easy, pleasing, and perfect to serve on nights when you don't feel like cooking. This recipe is guaranteed to fill your family's tummies with warmth and goodness. For a special effect, serve this dish surrounded with a bunch of grapes, and/or orange slices on each plate.

✧

Serves 4-5

12-ounces small shell pasta, cooked according to package directions and thoroughly drained

1 plus pound salad (very small) shrimp

5 tablespoons of canola or olive oil based butter spread

3-4 scallions diced or 3 tablespoons finely diced onion

1 lemon

2 thinly sliced garlic cloves or 1 teaspoon minced garlic

2 pinches of dried oregano (more if you'd like)

½ teaspoon dry or 2 teaspoons finely chopped fresh parsley

1½ cups frozen peas, thawed and drained, or 1½ cups chopped broccoli previously steamed or boiled until tender and easily pierced with a fork.

Parmesan cheese for sprinkling

1. In a medium saucepan or skillet melt the canola butter spread over medium heat, squeeze in all the juice from the lemon into the pan and then add the garlic, shrimp, oregano and parsley. Heat and stir all of these ingredients until hot.

2. Lower the heat to medium low and then add the cooked pasta and veggies to the shrimp mixture. Stir the entire mixture several times with a rubber spatula or large spoon ensuring that all of the ingredients until they are completely coated and hot.

3. Divide the Shrimpy Noodles between plates, and then top each serving with a sprinkle of Parmesan cheese. Serve with purple grapes or orange slices; either placed on the side of or around the edges of each plate.

✧ ✧ ✧

⌒ VARIATION ⌒

✧ Boiled or steamed Brussels Sprouts can be added instead of the peas or broccoli. Simply cut the bottom stem off, tear off the dirty outer leaves, and then cut each into 2-4 small pieces. Boil or microwave the Brussels sprouts in water until tender and easily pierced with a fork or knife, and then add accordingly.

TIP:

💗 *Brussels Sprouts are high in both Vitamin C and fiber. Plus they are rather sweet for a vegetable, thus they make a terrific afternoon snack when served hot with butter (or canola-based butter spread) and a sprinkling of Parmesan cheese.*

Blueberry Gobble

Not only does this recipe offer a terrific way to use some of the wisely purchased fresh fruits that you stocked up on during the warmer months and froze, it only takes minutes to prepare. Brimming with an immensely yummy, comforting flavor, this recipe is especially welcome on rainy or snowy days and is a super after school snack or dessert. Warm any leftovers for a quick breakfast and watch the smiles appear on sleepy faces.

✧

TIP:

♥ *Blueberries burst with immunity building agents and vitamins that help promote attention, focus, and overall brain functions, while oats provide the necessary fibers that help to regulate our bodies. Hence serving any combination of these two helps to maintain healthy bodies while improving clarity, focus and the attention necessary to learn and grow.*

✧

Preheat oven to 350° Fahrenheit   **Serves 6**

6-7 cups blueberries (preferably previously frozen, so that the natural sugars secrete into the juice once thawed. If using fresh fruit, no worries, it will taste just as wonderful)

½ cup oats (quick or old fashioned)

2½ tablespoons minute tapioca

⅓ cup flour

¼ cup brown sugar, packed firmly or brown sugar substitute

½-1 teaspoon cinnamon

¼ cup canola oil

1. Thoroughly grease a 2-quart casserole dish, or 9x9-inch pan with pan
spray, butter or margarine.

2. Thaw the frozen berries on high in
the microwave for 4-6 minutes or
until juicy.

3. Pour the fruit and juices into the
prepared dish, add the tapioca, and
mix thoroughly. Cover the dish with
a cloth or paper towel and allow
ingredients to sit for 10-15 minutes.

4. Mix the dry ingredients and cinnamon into another bowl, add the
canola oil, and then mix with a fork
until crumbly.

5. Sprinkle the oat mixture all over the
top of the fruit and bake for 30-40
minutes or until the crumbs begin
to brown and the juices are bubbly.
Serve hot or cold.

✧ ✧ ✧

ᥫ᭡ VARIATION ᥫ᭡

✧ Substitute 6-7 cups fresh or freshly
frozen blackberries or pitted, sweet
dark cherries for the blueberries.
A combination of fresh or freshly
frozen peaches and berries; cherries
and/or apricots also work well.
Additionally, if pomegranates are
available, absolutely add a ½ cup
in with the berries to enhance the
nutritional benefits. Pomegranates
are one of Mother Nature's healthiest
offerings and the kids can help by
picking the seeds out of the shell for
you.

HINTS

🌺 The best time to
purchase blueberries is
when they are placed
on sale in bulk, such as
2-5 pound containers.
These sales usually
occur in the middle
of the spring season
and toward the end
of July. Simply rinse
them off with water,
and then allow them
to dry or pat dry them
with a paper towel and
pour them into large,
freezer-safe plastic
bags. Freeze them
accordingly and use at
will.

🌺 This recipe makes a
super alternative to
cereal for breakfast,
when made in advance
the night before.
Simply scoop an
individual serving
into a bowl, heat
for a minute in the
microwave, and serve
with warm milk if
you'd like.

🌺 Served hot or cold
with a dollop of yogurt
on top to make an
extraordinarily light,
but special dessert.

Oats To Go Cakes

Are you in need of recipes to replace those dry, starchy, artificially flavored toaster bars or sugar-saturated breakfast bars with? Have you placed a store-bought "energy bar" into your kid's lunch box, only to find these same bars, partially eaten, in a jacket pocket later in the day? What a waste of hard earned funds! These awesome tasting mini cakes are fantastic alternatives, fabulously easy to prepare and will be enjoyed for years to come.

✧

Makes approximately 12 individual cakes

3 cups quick oats

3 cups flour

1-1½ teaspoons cinnamon
 (optional)

1½ teaspoons baking soda

¼ teaspoon salt

⅓ cup dark brown sugar

4½ cups milk

½ cup canola oil

1½ cups raisins, blueberries,
 cherries and/or chopped nuts

Butter, margarine or oil for
 cooking the cakes

HINT

❦ If using dried fruit, such as raisins or chopped apricots, for best flavor it is suggested to soak them in very hot water for ten minutes before mixing into food. This will plump the fruits, making them more palatable. Often when dried fruits get too hard, they don't taste as good and could discourage your kids from enjoying their benefits.

1. In a medium bowl, mix the sugar, milk and butter thoroughly together. In a larger bowl, mix the oats, flour, baking soda, salt and cinnamon together. Stir the fruits and/or nuts into the dry ingredients.

2. Add the milk mixture to the dry ingredients and stir until combined. There may be a few small lumps in the batter that will dissolve when cooked.

3. Heat approximately 2 tablespoons butter, margarine, or oil in a large frying pan or on a griddle over medium to high heat or until hot. You can test the heat by sprinkling a drop or 2 of water onto the pan; if it sizzles the pan is hot enough.

4. Using ¼ cup of batter at a time, pour the batter into rounded circles into the pan. When the tops begins to bubble, flip the individual cakes over and continue cooking for about 30-60 seconds or until the bottom is golden. Place the cooked cakes on a plate to cool.

5. Add more butter or margarine to the pan as needed until all batter has been cooked.

6. Wrap each cake individually in plastic wrap, and then place the cakes into a freezer-safe bag and freeze.

7. When desired, take 1 cake per person out of the bag, remove the plastic wrapping and toast it until thoroughly heated. A medium-dark setting on the toaster oven works best.

8. Once the cakes have heated, your kids can then spread butter or chunky preserves across the top and enjoy them on their way to the school bus stop. Or spread a tablespoon of peanut butter and ½ tablespoon of preserves atop each, fold in half and wrap in plastic wrap for a snack later in the day. A tasty, personal favorite is to serve these with apple butter and sliced bananas.

Homespun Potato Chips

Let's face it, that old advertisement for potato chips says it all: "You can't eat just one!" But do you really need those "super-sized" bags in your home, tempting this mindless, fattening activity of continuously reaching deeper into the bag for more? Preparing your own batch is a terrific way to start making better food decisions for your kids, at a lower price. Homespun potato chips supply the same crunchy, salty delight as those prepackaged varieties; they just don't have the excess fat required for in the frying process nor the added packaging cost.

✧

2-3 servings (average serving is 14-16 chips)

---

1 large russet or Idaho potato   Sea salt to taste
(peeled or unpeeled)

1. Wash the potatoes thoroughly. If you prefer to peel the potatoes, do so after washing and then rinse again under cool water. Slice potatoes into 35-45 thin slices using a Mandolin, thin slicing wheel of a food processor, or very sharp knife.

2. Thoroughly grease a glass microwave plate with pan spray and then sprinkle a small amount of salt all over the plate.

3. Place the potato slices side by side on the prepared microwave plate. Make sure that the slices do not overlap and that the thicker slices are placed in the middle of the plate.

4. Microwave the potatoes on high for 5-7 minutes depending on your microwave, as all cook differently. Once the potatoes begin turn golden, remove them from the microwave. Immediately slide them off the plate and into a bowl, sprinkle a pinch more salt on top, shake the bowl slightly to distribute the salt and then taste and lightly salt again if you wish. Allow to cool and serve. Store any leftovers wrapped in tin foil to maintain the crunch.

✧ ✧ ✧

ᏋᏉ VARIATIONS ᏉᏋ

✧ Substitute a sweet potato or yam for the baking potato, and if you want, sprinkle these chips with a very small amount of cinnamon sugar and just a pinch of salt.

✧ For BBQ-flavored potato chips, sprinkle a small amount of BBQ seasoning lightly over the potato slices before placing the plate into the microwave and cook accordingly.

Meet Ms. Maple A. Squash

And a lovely lady she is. She is commonly found dressed in a beautiful dark green outer coat, which resembles the tone of evergreen trees on a cool autumn eve. However, once sliced open, her color peaks in a soft, golden tone. She adores being heated with a little blend of amber sweetness, for it brings out a luscious, comforting essence to all that relish in her company.

✧

TIPS:

♥ *Acorn squash is filled with vitamin C, potassium, manganese, folic acid, which helps to increase our metabolisms and energy levels, and omega 3 fatty acids which helps increase brain power and promote healthy hearts.*

♥ *Pure Maple Syrup contains manganese, which is a great source of energy production and antioxidants; and this syrup contains Zinc, which is good for maintaining a healthy heart. A plus is that these two minerals are quite beneficial to our immune systems.. Just remember 2 tablespoons is an adequate serving, more is too much.*

✧

HINT

Although the choice is yours, please take into account that the price of prepackaged candy or cakes/cookies is about the same as this delicious delicacy. Yet the difference is that most prepackaged snacks contain minimal nutrients, whereby this one is loaded with healthful benefits. This recipe is also a scrumptious alternative to those prepackaged veggies with sauce added, when prepared as side dish to a meal.

Preheat oven to 350° Fahrenheit   **Serves 2**

1 acorn squash

2 teaspoons butter or margarine

2 tablespoons pure maple syrup

1. Fill a 9x13-inch pan partially with warm water. (About half way up the side of the pan is fine, but not more.)

2. Slice the acorn in half crosswise, and then scrap the seeds and fibers away from the center with a spoon.

3. Place a teaspoon of butter into the hollow center, and then add 1 tablespoon of pure maple syrup on top of the butter.

4. Gently place each half into the prepared pan, so that they remain upright and then bake the squash for 25-30 minutes or until tender and easily pierced with a fork.

5. Serve with a spoon and enjoy.

HINTS

🍎 There is a distinct flavor difference between pure maple syrup and artificially flavored varieties. Despite the fact that pure maple syrup is pricier, its flavor is pure and strong. On the other hand, artificially flavored varieties are weak in flavor, for they are primarily made from high fructose corn syrup and flavoring agents, which may cause the use of more in order to gain the exquisite flavor.

🍎 To ensure that the pure maple syrup does not expire, it is best to store it in the refrigerator.

Dirty Spotted Dog
(Rice Pudding)

Thick, rich and good for you, diverse varieties of rice-based pudding have been a favorite food for sustenance and flavor throughout centuries. However, it was one of the first settlers in America's Old West who thought it resembled a Dalmatian puppy when prepared with raisins, and fondly gave it it's nickname 'Spotted Pup'. Oh, but once some of the more seasoned chuck wagon cooks began mixing a bit of spice into this favored delight, it was referred to as Dirty Spotted Dog. Why? Because, the spices turned the fluffy white rice to the color of the dust, that blew in the wake of the wagon trail.

TIP:

♥ *Rice is a natural source of energy, Vitamin D, calcium, fiber, iron, thiamine (B1) and riboflavin (B2). It has been found too help lower high blood pressure, hypertension, and is a whole grain that can aid in preventing cancer.*

HINT

This marvelous dish can be served as an alternative to prepackaged cereals, and it makes a terrific snack for later in the day or night. Although thicker than many sugar-laden varieties, the flavor is fabulous, soothing, and filling enough to satisfy until the next meal is served.

Makes 6-7 servings

1 cup long grain rice, uncooked

One 12 ounce can evaporated milk

1¾ cups milk

¼ cup brown sugar, lightly packed

1 teaspoon vanilla

¾ teaspoon cinnamon

2 dashes nutmeg

¾ cup raisins

3-4 teaspoons butter or canola-based butter spread

1. Mix all of the ingredients, but the butter, together in a medium sized saucepan.

2. Heat the ingredients over medium heat, gradually bringing it to a simmer, while stirring the ingredients frequently.

3. Once the ingredients begin to simmer (slightly bubble), reduce the heat to medium low and continue to stir the ingredients frequently to prevent a thick skin from developing.

4. Once the mixture begins to thicken, keep stirring it and reduce the heat a little bit more.

5. Making sure that the ingredients are still simmering, reduce the heat to low, partially cover the pot and continue to frequently stir for about 20 minutes or until the pudding is thick and the rice is tender.

6. Remove the pudding from the heat, and then stir the butter into the pudding.

7. Pour the pudding into a large bowl and serve hot or cold with a little bit of milk.

8. Cover the bowl in plastic wrap and store excess pudding for up to 4 days in the refrigerator.

HIGH ALTITUDE TIP Know that the higher in altitude, the longer this pudding will need to simmer until the rice is tender.

RISK FACTORS OF OVER-EATING

Risk Factors of Over-Eating

Overeating on a daily basis can cause excess weight gain, especially in children!

❧

1. **Addiction:** The act of overeating on a regular basis can become addictive. A body gets accustomed to being over filled with food, and in an effort to sustain this feeling; one eats more and more and more until the body can no longer move or begins to shut down. Just like an alcohol or drug addiction, overeating on a regular basis becomes a revolving cycle, until the cycle is changed or stopped.

2. **Ostracized:** Unfortunately there are social stigmas associated with being overweight or obese. Many overweight people become isolated, trying to protect themselves from abuses inflicted by others. They feel unworthy and empty, and may attempt to fill this emptiness with food. This is particularly true in children.

3. **Low Self Esteem:** "I am ugly, I cannot change, and I am a bad person because I am too fat! This is a repetitive cycle. I can't do this or that because I am too fat. I am not acceptable."

4. **Eating Disorder:** Occasionally in an attempt to alleviate the emotional pain of being overweight, some children (and adults) may try to take off the excess weight by binging and purging (Bulimia), or starving him or herself (Anorexia Nervosa). These diseases will deplete the body of the nutrients necessary to maintain a healthy lifestyle and the one suffering from such may develop various medical and emotional disorders as a result.

5. **Obesity:** Another type of Eating Disorder is the result of gaining more than 25-30 percent of one's average weight based on height and age. His or her body is no longer able to maintain a healthy, active lifestyle and devastating medical conditions are often the result.

6. **Heart Problems:** Just like too much of anything that is not very good for us, when a parent or guardian serves too much fast, processed and prepackaged food on a regular basis it begins to affect the whole body, especially the heart. It has to beat faster in order to pump the blood through its arteries. Unfortunately when it begins to beat too fast, it can also turn itself off, and

shut down bodily functions.

7. **High Cholesterol:** Although occasionally related to heredity or various bodily ailments, this condition is usually the result of over eating salty, fat filled foods. When this type of diet is combined with little or no exercise, then a body runs a higher risk of developing high cholesterol and possibly a resulting heart disease.

8. **Breathing Problems:** Heavy breathing or asthma is likely to develop, making it difficult to complete small physical tasks without the assistance of an inhaler or something more drastic, such as an oxygen tank. Just walking to the end of the block or up a set of stairs can become extremely difficult, as you must breathe harder to get the oxygen to the lungs.

9. **Diabetes:** Not only may overeating result in daily shots of insulin to control the diabetes, but it can eventually lead to amputations of various body parts as children become adults. In addition, the high costs of medications often gobble up excess funds or the ability to pay bills on time.

10. **Lack of Physical Activity:** It is well known that the more a person overeats, the less likely they are to be physically active. Instead they become more lethargic, flabby and possibly ill.

11. **Weight Gain Continues:** The more a child gets used to overeating, the more weight he/she gains throughout the growing process. Hence, the likelihood of an overweight child, becoming an overweight/obese adult increases significantly. In fact, a recent study at Georgetown University has found that more than one-half of all 6 year olds and older who are obese as children grow up to be obese adults.

12. **The Cost Gets Higher:** I have heard many complain about the rising cost of health care. Yet, some of these same people are severely overweight and so are their children. Therefore, I believe it is important for you to know that it has been researched and reported by The Washington Post and affiliates that in 2008 the cost of medical expenses and loss of productivity related to obesity just in the United States was approximately $177 Billion; $14 Billion was spent on medical expenses for overweight and obese children. Also, research has shown that an obese person will spend about $1400 more per year on health care than an average sized person. And, when you consider that the World Health Organization classifies over 400 million adults, and over 20 million kids under the age of 5 years old as obese, the cost for such rises significantly higher.

ADJUSTING THE AMOUNTS OF FOOD SERVED

Adjusting the Amounts of Food Served

⟨◆⟩

O ne of the most important ways to induce weight loss, and/or prevent excess weight gain in your children is to feed them less by adjusting the serving sizes of the foods you prepare or have had prepared (such as take-out). Medical experts recommend that a typical serving size is equivalent to the size of the fist or palm of the individual being served; thus, use this measurement as your guide. Literally, fill each plate individually according to this measurement, and stop placing all the serving bowls and plates on the table from which all can serve themselves. This small act alone helps to eliminate extra large servings and the temptation for a second helping. Also, begin to cook just a little bit less, such as boiling three potatoes to be mashed instead of four; or prepare four burgers on the grill, rather than six or seven, as one burger per person is enough. If your loved ones still want more, remind them that there is more salad or a large bowl of fresh fruit available to fulfill their desire for more food. Additionally, when you are cooking a large batch of food with the intention of storing some of it for another day, remind your family that the excess is for another meal, not now. End of subject!

Another issue to consider is the size of the plates and bowls used. Researchers at both Cornell University and Pennsylvania State University have found that one of the best ways to decrease the size of servings is to alter the size of the dishes used. The larger the plate or bowl, the more food we tend to take, thus, smaller bowls and plates result in smaller portions. While this may be so, do not assume that you need to run out and purchase smaller plates and bowls, for you do not! Instead, get a bit creative when filling your plates and bowls. For instance, when you notice a smidgen of empty space or half-filled bowl after dishing out adequate serving sizes, you can always make them look fuller by adding a slice or small bunch of colorful fresh fruit such as oranges, grapes, or berries.

Although creatively filling serving plates and adjusting serving sizes may initially be challenged by your loved ones, keep in mind that large servings are a definite contributor to excessive weight gain, especially in children. Large servings cause the stomach to expand more, resulting in a feeling of being too full to move, play, or work. Additionally, once the stomach gets used to such expansion, this feeling becomes expected whenever one eats, thus contributing to excess weight gain. Teaching your kids to recognize when they have had enough to eat is a fabulous way to reduce unwanted weight gain. Many years ago, a friend's mother taught me just how to do this. She instructed me to recognize the slight feeling of a bulge in my belly against my pants or skirt as an indication that my body has had enough food during the meal. Teach your kids to recognize this feeling, as if their bodies are talking to them and telling them to stop eating because it have had enough. This is a great way to begin promoting good eating habits, and decreasing the old habit of overeating simply because there is more food to be devoured.

And if the older kids begin to complain (which initially they most likely will), remind them of your love while pointing to the bowl of fruit or salad to fulfill their want for more food. If the complaining continues, simply remind them that: *"I'm sorry honey, but we are changing the way we eat because I love you and want you to have more energy to play and enjoy life with!"* They may curse at you or respond with *"Ohhh Mommm,"* but just smile, stick to your words, and watch the respect grow.

Lastly, an important concept to keep in mind is that good, homemade food produces many positive results, including a dash of an ego boost for the cook. It feels so good and warm when we see our families and friends grabbing for that extra large or second helping. However, although it personally feels great to see and hear such praise, accept it and be pleased with yourself; but do not let your ego get in the way of developing better eating habits in your household. One serving of each food prepared is enough. If they want more, tell them they can have more salad, veggies or a piece of fresh fruit, rather than an extra helping of macaroni and cheese, a 2nd burger or another piece of pie.

Pizza

These succulent "Italian Pies" are very inviting, but how much of a good thing is too much? Is one slice enough for a meal or are two or three slices an adequate serving size? Although this decision depends on the size and type of pizza (NY thin crust vs. deep dish) as well as the age of your children, one slice should be sufficient for younger children, two medium-sized slices for preteens and a maximum of three medium-sized slices for older kids, but no more, especially when you have other foods (salad, not bread sticks) available to satisfy their hunger. Also keep in mind that the serving size can increase or decrease depending on the size of the pizza slices, as well as how a child eats the pizza. (For example, do they leave most of the crust on their plate?)

✧

TIP:

♥ *Spinach helps build strong bones, eyes and minds. Adding just a bit of finely minced spinach to tomato-based sauces is a great way to add an extra dose of veggies to your family's food choices.*

✧

HINT

Pizza provides a great opportunity to teach your kids how to recognize when their body has had enough to eat. Inform them that once they first begin to feel a slight belly bulge against their pants or skirt, that this feeling is their body talking to them and telling them that it has had enough. Also, have your kids drink a glass of water or milk before meals are served. Both beverages will slightly fill the belly, thus decreasing the want for extra servings.

Easy Crust:

1 frozen *unbaked* whole wheat bread loaf

Flat bread or Your favorite store-bought pizza crust

If using bread dough, allow it to thaw and double in bulk. Once the dough's bulk has doubled, punch it down and stretch/pull it until it fits a 12-inch pizza pan previously greased with pan spray. Prepare the sauce and toppings and proceed accordingly.

If using flat bread, simply place the bread onto a greased cookie sheet. Prepare the sauce and toppings and proceed accordingly.

If using a store bought crust, follow the instructions listed and then prepare the sauce and toppings and proceed accordingly.

Sauce:

¾-1 cup tomato sauce

3-4 tablespoons tomato paste

2 tablespoons olive oil

1-2 teaspoons finely diced onion

2 teaspoons sugar or ½ teaspoon baking soda

¼ teaspoon oregano

Pinch of rosemary and/or thyme

¼ teaspoon sweet basil

2 garlic cloves minced or 2 teaspoons minced garlic

3-4 tablespoons finely minced spinach, depending on size of pizza (frozen, thawed and patted dry or fresh)

1 small zucchini, thinly sliced

1-2 teaspoons olive oil to brush crust with

HINT

Double the sauce and store half in a freezer-safe bag, and freeze it for use at another time.

Pizza continued on next page

Pizza continued

Toppings:

1-1½ cups of chopped cooked meats and/or diced and sliced veggies

2-3 cups grated mozzarella and/or provolone

1-1½ tablespoons Parmesan, optional

1. Mix all the sauce ingredients into a bowl. Allow this mixture to rest for 30-45 minutes, ensuring that the individual ingredient flavors blend together.

2. Once the sauce ingredients have blended, spread them evenly on top of the crust and then sprinkle toppings of choice evenly over the sauce.

3. Fold the edges of the crust slightly over itself and tuck it in to seal. Brush 1-2 teaspoons of olive oil all over the crust's edge. Sprinkle the Parmesan cheese on top before baking.

4. Bake the pizza for 20-30 minutes or until the cheese has melted and bubbly. Slice into 8 pieces using a serrated knife or pizza wheel and serve while hot.

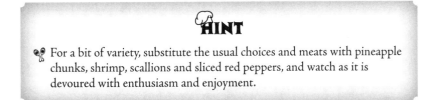

HINT

For a bit of variety, substitute the usual choices and meats with pineapple chunks, shrimp, scallions and sliced red peppers, and watch as it is devoured with enthusiasm and enjoyment.

True Blue Muffin

Bursting with flavor, this recipe is a fabulous early morning alternative to prepackaged breakfast cakes, toaster bars or doughnuts. These are also super to serve as a tasty mid-morning snack or as an afternoon treat. This special recipe provides an opportunity to practice and perfect the art of controlling your ego' while restraining yourself from allowing second helpings. The praise you receive will be loud and wonderful, and the "yums," "oohs" and "ahhs" will tempt you to give in to pleas for more; as it feels so good when your efforts are enjoyed and appreciated. However, you love your kids and know that one serving of a baked treat per day is enough. Thus, when the times get tough, remind yourself of that love and refuse to give into pleas for more, including your own.

✧

Preheat oven to 375° Fahrenheit

Makes 8 large muffins or 42-48 mini muffins
(4-6 mini muffins is an average serving depending on size and age)

HINTS

- ❦ Although cooking/baking times are supplies, all ovens cook differently; therefore always check a product for doneness before removing from the oven.

- ❦ Muffins are a type of cake, so remind your kids when they want cookies or cake later in the day, that they have already indulged in one baked treat for the day and another is not necessary. To temper their sweet tooth and hunger, offer a bowl of plain yogurt drizzled with a teaspoon of honey or a couple homemade Happystacks (page 199) instead.

Continued on next page

True Blue Muffin continued

Topping:

2 tablespoons sugar or sugar substitute

2 tablespoons flour

½ teaspoon cinnamon

1 teaspoon butter or margarine

Mix these ingredients together with a fork until crumbly and set aside

Muffins:

½ cup (1 stick) canola oil based butter spread or margarine

1½ cups sugar

1 tablespoon vanilla

4 cups flour

5 teaspoons baking powder

2 cups milk

1½-3 cups fresh or freshly frozen blueberries

⅔ cup chopped walnuts (optional)

HIGH ALTITUDE TIP — Add ¼ cup more flour and 2 extra tablespoons milk to the muffins.

1. Thoroughly mix the margarine, sugar, vanilla, milk, flour and baking powder together in a mixing bowl.

2. Slowly add the blueberries the batter and mix them in at low speed until all ingredients are thoroughly incorporated, but still with a short supply of small lumps lingering in the batter.

3. Thoroughly grease 8 sections of a large muffin pan, or 42 sections in two mini muffin pans with pan spray, butter or margarine. (You may need to grease a couple more sections in the mini muffin pans.)

4. Divide the batter evenly between the prepared muffin sections, and then sprinkle the cinnamon mixture evenly on top of each.

5. Bake 12-35 minutes (depending on muffin size) or until they are golden and feel firm on top or until inserted knife or toothpick comes out clean.

6. Remove the muffins from the pan within a minute or two to prevent further baking. Allow the steam to evaporate for a couple more minutes and wrap large muffins individually in plastic wrap. If baking mini-muffins, wrap them in small packages of 6-12 muffins and store in an airtight plastic container or freezer-safe bag and freeze.

HINTS

❧ No, there are no eggs in this recipe!

❧ To store muffins for future snacks, place wrapped muffins into freezer-safe bags and freeze accordingly. Thaw naturally or remove the plastic wrapping and thaw on high in the microwave for a few seconds or until lukewarm to touch.

❧ Make a few large muffins and use the remaining batter for mini muffins to serve as after school snacks or late night snacks.

✧ ✧ ✧

∾ VARIATIONS ∾

✧ Raspberries, huckleberries, chopped sweet dark cherries; diced peaches or diced apples can be used in place of blueberries. If using peaches or apples, add ½ teaspoon nutmeg to the batter. If using cherries, add 1 teaspoon almond extract to the batter.

Nutter Butter Sandwiches

Peanut butter sandwiches are an easy favorite, but did you know that one serving of peanut butter is literally only 2 tablespoons per day, and no more. And, adding jelly only increases the sugar content of these favorite sandwiches. Thus to decrease the intake of added sugars, adjust the sandwich ingredients to a healthier version, such as these listed below.

✧

TIP:

> ♥ *The reason why you hear so much about eating whole grain breads and cereals is that white bread is low in fiber and can cause damage to a body's intestines due to its high content of gluten. Additionally these varieties are usually high in fat, and contain excess sugar that may contribute to tooth decay. On the other hand, whole wheat and whole grain breads and cereals are loaded with fiber, iron and various energy producing vitamins that help reduce the risk of diabetes, coronary disease and cancer.*

✧

Per Sandwich:

A. Two slices whole wheat or whole grain bread (cut the edges off for the little ones). Spread 2 tablespoons or less peanut butter onto 1 slice of bread and then spread 1-1½ tablespoons of previously made chunky preserves, or place fresh fruit (1-2 tablespoons berries or ½ an apple, peeled and sliced) on top of the peanut butter and top with remaining bread slice.

B. Two slices whole wheat or whole grain bread (cut the edges off for the little ones). Slice half of a banana onto the peanut butter, and then drizzle 1 teaspoon of honey on top of the bananas. Sprinkle 1 tablespoon of raisins (previously soaked and patted dry) on top of the honey and top with the remaining bread slice.

C. Two slices whole wheat or whole grain bread (cut the edges off for the little ones). Slice 1 medium-length celery rib into 3-4 pieces and then slice each into 2-3 little sticks. Or Sprinkle a tablespoon or less of raisins or dried cherries (previously soaked and patted dry) on top of the peanut butter, and place the celery sticks, inside down, evenly across the other ingredients and top with the remaining bread slice.

HINT

To prevent browning of apple or banana slices, drizzle a tiny bit of lemon juice over the sliced fruit before adding to the sandwich.

Giant Chipper Oat Cookies

Cookies, cookies, cookies; who make the best cookies? Grandmothers, moms and dads, with the kids' help, of course! Kids love to eat cookies, and many enjoy helping make these little treats of sweetness. Unfortunately, controlling the amount they eat can be frustrating, as the average serving really is only *2-3 cookies a day*, not per meal. But did you know that a giant cookie is approximately the same size as three average-sized cookies, and can take a child an entire day to eat. Many, especially little ones, want to savor the taste and make it last as long as possible, so they nibble a little bite here and another bite there.

✧

TIPS:

💜 *Adding oats to various edible delights, especially to baked treats, is one of the best foods choices you can make for your family. Naturally filled with health enhancing vitamins, lots of fiber, and much more protein than grains such as wheat, barley, corn and rice; makes oats (Quick and Old Fashioned) one of the 'Super Foods' for maintaining a healthy body and weight.*

💜 *As said, pomegranates are one of the healthiest of Mother Nature's offerings. The tiny seeds burst on the palate with an awesome flavor, while supplying the body with a natural dose of vitamins. Additionally, just picking out the individual seeds occupies empty time and is a great means for getting the little ones into the kitchen to help, while keeping them occupied and out of your way.*

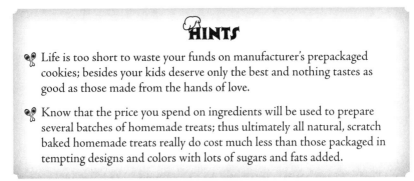

HINTS

🔖 Life is too short to waste your funds on manufacturer's prepackaged cookies; besides your kids deserve only the best and nothing tastes as good as those made from the hands of love.

🔖 Know that the price you spend on ingredients will be used to prepare several batches of homemade treats; thus ultimately all natural, scratch baked homemade treats really do cost much less than those packaged in tempting designs and colors with lots of sugars and fats added.

Preheat oven to 375° Fahrenheit	Makes 8-9 large cookies

⅔ cup canola oil

½ cup (1 stick) butter

¾ cup brown sugar

¾ cup sugar or sugar substitute

1 tablespoon vanilla

3 cups Quick Oats

2 large eggs or equivalent amount liquid egg substitute

1½ cups flour

1 teaspoon baking soda

1½-2 cups (9-12-ounces) semi-sweet chocolate chips

Additions, if desired: ¾ cup fresh pomegranate seeds, chopped walnuts, pecans, almonds, hazelnuts, raisins or craisins

HIGH ALTITUDE TIP Add an additional 2 tablespoons of flour and decrease the baking soda by slightly indenting your finger into the ingredient while leveling the measuring spoon.

1. Cream together the oil, butter, vanilla and sugars.

2. Add the remaining ingredients, adding 1 egg at a time while mixing. Mix all the ingredients until thoroughly incorporated.

3. Thoroughly grease two or three cookie sheets with pan spray, butter or margarine.

4. Use an ice cream scoop or a ⅓-cup, scoop up individual cookies and then drop them onto the prepared cookie sheets. With the palm of your hand, slightly flatten the top of each cookie.

5. Bake for 12-14 minutes or until the edges begin to brown. Remove the cookies from the pan after 2-3 minutes and wrap individually in plastic wrap to maintain crunchy edges and soft centers.

✧ ✧ ✧

✑ VARIATION ✑

✧ Add 2 teaspoons cinnamon and ½ teaspoon nutmeg while mixing the flour and oats into the batter. Raisins, previously soaked and patted dry taste superb in this recipe.

Cheesy Ease

Granted there are numerous inexpensive boxes and containers of easily prepared foods available to make your life as a parent/guardian easier; however nothing beats the taste of homemade food, made all naturally from scratch. In consideration that Macaroni and Cheese is a childhood favorite, many kids have a tendency to eat much more than they should in an effort to sustain the comforting warmth. Yet are those prepackaged varieties the best choice you can make, especially when a homemade version tastes much better, is very easy to prepare and the serving sizes can be adjusted accordingly, rather than predetermined in a container. Besides, homemade varieties often produce leftovers, which can easily be reheated or mixed with additional ingredients another day. Prepackaged varieties do not include such luxuries, as the noodles may get too hard to enjoy at another time.

✧

Preheat oven to 325° Fahrenheit   **Serves 4-6**

HINT

- Please know that Mac & Cheese is not a good choice of a snack for those who are already overweight, and who do not get much exercise. Therefore, when making better food decisions for your kids, refrain from having prepackaged varieties available and only serve this comforting favorite as a meal or as a side dish to a meal.

2 cups uncooked macaroni or small shaped pasta such as shells, wheels or small Rotini

2¼ cups milk

1 egg

2¼ cups, (10 ounces) grated Colby, Cheddar, Monterrey Jack, Swiss or a combo of both mozzarella and provolone

2 tablespoons cold butter or margarine

2 teaspoons finely minced onion or scallions

Pinch of dry mustard (optional)

½ teaspoon garlic powder

¼ teaspoon nutmeg

Salt and pepper to taste

1-2 tablespoons cold butter

1. Thoroughly grease an 8x8-inch pan with pan spray, butter or margarine.

2. Mix the egg thoroughly into the milk. Add the spices to the milk mixture and mix thoroughly.

3. In the prepared pan start layering the ingredients by evenly spreading half of the uncooked pasta, then sprinkle half the cheese on top of the pasta, dotting the top of the cheese with 1 tablespoon of the butter. Pour half of the milk mixture over this layer and repeat this layering process with the remaining ingredients, ending with a layer of cheese and dotted (tiny pieces) butter.

4. Bake for 35-40 minutes and serve immediately.

✧ ✧ ✧

～ VARIATIONS ～

✧ Use a 9x9-inch pan when adding veggies, fruits, and/or meats.

✧ Add ½-¾ cup peas, diced green or red peppers, tomatoes, chopped broccoli, cauliflower, zucchini or blueberries, pomegranates, raisins, and/or diced apple to the layers. (If adding fruits, do not add the mustard, garlic, and onion powder; instead, add ½ teaspoon of cinnamon and a dash of nutmeg to the egg mixture.)

✧ Simply mix 2-3 tablespoons finely minced fresh or frozen spinach (thawed and patted dry) into the egg/milk mixture and proceed accordingly.

✧ Mix 2 teaspoons minced jalapenos and a couple drops of hot sauce into the egg/milk mixture and proceed accordingly.

✧ Add 1-1½ cups lightly cooked ground beef, Italian sausage, turkey, drained tuna fish, cooked, flaked salmon, chopped shrimp, lobster or crabmeat under the cheese when layering.

Food as a Reward

⟨ ❧ ⟩

One of the best decisions you can make for your kids is to avoid using food as a reward. Many parents reward children with food for good behavior, improved grades, as a bribe for completing chores, and so on. Unfortunately these types of rewards can develop the habit of expecting a food reward whenever the child accomplishes something. Unfortunately, the use of food as a reward often carries over into adulthood, whereby children who were rewarded with food often grow up to reward themselves with food.

Instead of bribing your children with a fat-filled, sugary treat or a trip to the fast food restaurant, why not show your love and appreciation for something well done by rewarding them with an extra hug and words of praise. Tell them how proud you are that they were so good and acted so very "grown up" while at the doctor's office or store. Praise goes a long way mom and dad; it builds confidence and helps to promote positive and productive attitudes. Fast and/or junk food only go to the gut!

Another option is to treat your children to a special walk, physically active game such as catch or tag or even be an active participant in a video game. You can also take them to the video store to pick out a movie of their choice. The options for rewarding your kids are endless and most do not involve food. You see all a reward really takes is lots of smiles, hugs, maybe a few tears, a few words of appreciation and some personal, one on one attention.

⟨ ❧ ⟩

Better Choices for Flavor and Health

❧

One of the best food related decisions you can make is to cut back on fatty, sugar infused and salty commercially prepared and/or prepackaged foods. These foods are commonly found in the snack aisles at the grocery store, in some varieties of frozen, boxed or previously prepared foods (e.g. canned fruits, frozen dinners, prepackaged side dishes) as well as in most Take-out and Fast Food restaurants. Sure these choices are cheap, tasty, filling, and definitely much too easy to simply ignore. But when fed to children on a regular basis (several times per week), they can induce unnecessary weight gain. They are also significantly more expensive than homemade food, although initially the price may not appear to be.

Know that one of the greatest choices you can make for decreasing the amount of fats, salts and sugars consumed by your children is to stop frequenting fast food restaurants or calling a restaurant for a take-out order so often. Who wouldn't want the quick, easy fix of a snack or meal without having to do any prep, dish washing or clean up afterwards? These foods definitely make your life easier. Yet, when your child/children are already overweight, are these really the foods that help to promote weight loss and healthy hearts?

Think about it honestly. Are fast foods and take-out really the type of food you want your children indulging in several times per week while their bodies and minds are developing and growing? Is this the type of food that promotes healthy weight, while building strong minds and bones? I would think not! Most of these foods only supply a quick fix of flavors accentuated by grease, salt and sugar. So why not make these foods special, by serving them less frequently? Your family can choose one day or night per week for take-out, pizza or a trip to the fast food restaurant, but not more than one; especially when you have more nutritional choices available at home. Also, remember, if you choose to eat and serve poor food choices, then your kids and most likely your children's kids are more likely to do the same.

In summary, children will eat the food choices that you provide for them. Therefore, make the best choices that you can to ensure their health, happiness and life. Look at the list of ingredients or choices you are currently making and moderately alter them in favor of varieties that promote health and flavor, rather than just a quick fix. For example, sliced apples are a terrific inexpensive snack, but when served with a sugary (caramel) dipping sauce, the apple's nutritional value is forfeited with each dunk into the sugary, artificially flavored sauce. However, when you cut an apple into slices and serve it as is or with a piece of cheese, then the nutritional value remains high. The choice is yours mom and dad, so make it the best that you can, rather than the most convenient.

Jiffy Chicken Stir

Imagine that it is the end of a long day, and the last thing you feel like doing is cooking dinner. Sure, calling out for 'take-out' may be an easy solution, but definitely not economical, or the healthiest choice for your family. So what do you do? You throw together a flavorful meal in no time at all; and enjoy the moment with your children as they share their tales of the day and dreams for the future.

✧

Serves 4-6

2 teaspoons minced garlic

1 bunch green onions, diced

1 zucchini, thinly sliced

1 cup chopped broccoli

1-2 carrots, thinly sliced or grated

2 large celery sticks, cut in half crosswise and then sliced into long thin pieces

¾ cup frozen peas, thawed

1 pound fresh or freshly frozen and thawed skinless chicken breast or thighs, cut into 1-2 inch pieces

2 cups water

2 cups minute brown or long grain rice

½ cup Teriyaki sauce

1 teaspoon Worcestershire sauce

1. Heat the oil in a large skillet over medium high for about 30-60 seconds. Lower the temperature to medium, and add the chicken, garlic and veggies to the skillet.

2. Cook the chicken and veggies for 5-10 minutes, stirring the mixture frequently to distribute the heat.

3. Stir the water, Teriyaki sauce and Worcestershire sauces into the chicken and heat the ingredients to a boil.

4. Once boiling, add the rice, lower the heat to low medium and cover the skillet. Allow the ingredients to mingle and simmer for 7-10 minutes.

5. 5. Once all ingredients are tender, remove the skillet from the heat, fluff the rice with a fork and serve.

✧ ✧ ✧

✑ VARIATIONS ✑

✧ 1 pound beef, pork or shrimp may be used in place of the chicken

✧ 1 cup of peas or 1-pound bag of mixed veggies can be used in place of the vegetables suggested

Ample Apple Browns

Filled with the twang of birds singing, crickets chirping, and the bright sun setting beyond open meadows, this countrified dish is supremely yummy; and it only takes a few minutes to prepare. Additionally this recipe provides a great way to use up leftover meat, such as ham, chicken or turkey.

✧

Serves 2-4 (Depending if served as a side dish or as a whole meal)

3 tablespoons olive oil or canola based butter spread

2 small sweet potatoes or yams

1½ small firm red apples

2 tablespoons diced onion

Sprinkle of nutmeg

Sea salt to taste

1 cup cubed ham, turkey or chicken, previously cooked and warmed

1. Thoroughly wash both the potatoes and apples (leave the skins on), cut them into slices, remove any apple seeds and then grate them together in a food processor.

2. Heat the oil in a large frying pan over medium-low high heat.

3. Add the potatoes, apples and onions to the pan, and then sprinkle them with a small amount of nutmeg and sea salt.

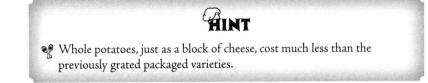

HINT

🍎 Whole potatoes, just as a block of cheese, cost much less than the previously grated packaged varieties.

4. Flip the potato apple mixture over after 2-3 minutes, and then sprinkle this side with a little more salt. (Make sure not to use too much salt, as the choice of meats will also naturally add some.)

5. Continue flipping the potatoes and apples over until they begin to brown. You may wish to add an additional small amount of oil or butter to the pan during the browning process.

6. Just before removing the potatoes from the pan, gently fold in preferred meat/poultry pieces,

7. Allow the meats to warm within the potatoes for a few seconds and then remove all from the heat and serve.

Nuggie Hugs
(Homemade Chicken Nuggets)

Kids love finger foods, and chicken nuggets are a particular favorite, especially among your younger children. These crunchy, little chicken bites are commonly found processed and prepackaged in most home freezers, on a school's weekly lunch menu and of course in the majority of fast food restaurants. Unfortunately, many previously prepared varieties contain minimal meat and lots of greasy, fried coating. However, homemade nuggets provide much more meat and minimal breading, and are wonderfully inexpensive and effortless to prepare. So why not spend some quality time with the kids in the kitchen, teaching them how to make these flavorful, little nuggets of childhood splendor, while gaining a few extra hugs in the process.

✧

Preheat oven to 375° Fahrenheit **Serves 6**

1½ pounds skinless, boneless chicken breasts

¾ cup flour

¾ cup buttermilk (or ¾ cup milk mixed with 1 tablespoon lemon juice or vinegar)

¾-1 cup finely crushed corn flakes

½ teaspoon garlic powder

¼ teaspoon onion powder

¼-½ teaspoon paprika (optional)

Pinch of dry parsley

Couple drops Tabasco® or hot sauce (optional)

Sea salt and pepper to taste

1. Line a cookie sheet with tin foil, and then place an oven rack or portable grill rack on top of the foil.

2. Grease the rack thoroughly with pan spray or butter.

3. Have the kids crush the corn flakes by first measuring the required amount, then placing them into a baggie and crushing them into the size of bread crumbs, while you wash the chicken.

4. Cut the chicken into 2-inch pieces.

5. Place the flour in a shallow bowl, add the spices and mix thoroughly. Place the buttermilk into another bowl and the crushed corn flakes into a third bowl.

6. Dredge the individual chicken pieces in flour. Shake off excess flour, and then dip each into the buttermilk and coat both sides. Next, dredge each nugget in the crushed corn flakes, tap off any excess against the inside of the bowl and place on the prepared baking rack.

7. Bake nuggets for 12-15 minutes. Remove them from the rack and serve as is or with choice of dips, such as BBQ sauce, ranch dressing, sweet and sour sauce or cheese sauce.

8. Freeze excess nuggets in a freezer safe baggie or airtight plastic container and reheat for a few minutes at 375° F in the oven or toaster oven for a quick meal.

HINT

This recipe also works well with zucchini slices, mushrooms and/or broccoli florets. So for variety, mix a few veggies into the batch of nuggets and make it a special crunchy meal for all to enjoy.

✧ ✧ ✧

⤳ VARIATIONS ⤶

✧ For spicy flavor, add ¼ teaspoon crushed red pepper flakes or a few more drops of Tabasco®.

✧ For an Italian flavor, add ¼-½ teaspoon Italian seasoning, plus a dash of garlic powder.

Suggested Dipping Sauces for Nuggets

Average serving is 2 tablespoons per person

✧

TIP:

💙 *Dipping sauces are just what the term implies-- a dip. Many use dips as if they are to be spooned/scooped onto the food product that it is enriching. This act not only overpowers the flavor of the primary food, but also packs on excess calories. For purposes of clarification, when making better food decisions for your kids, an example of the difference is: To dip is to dunk; to scoop is to mound the complementary food onto the primary food. Example, a sweet and sour sauce gets dunked into, whereas guacamole is scooped onto a corn chip or cracker. Thus, to prevent scooping of dips and sauces (as well as to stop the spreading of germs), I suggest you place a couple tablespoons of a dip onto each child's plate; rather than serving all of it in one bowl for each to help themselves from.*

✧

SWEET AND SOUR SAUCE

Also pairs scrumptiously with grilled poultry, pork, or fish.

Makes approximately 1 cup

One, 8-ounce can crushed pineapple	¼ cup orange juice or apricot nectar
1 tablespoon cornstarch	¼ cup BBQ sauce

1. Mix all the ingredients together in a saucepan, and heat them over medium high until the mixture begins to boil.

2. Reduce the heat to low and allow the ingredients to simmer. To prevent the bottom of the pan from burning, make sure to stir the ingredients constantly until the ingredients begin to thicken.

3. Once the sauce has thickened, remove the saucepan from heat and allow this sauce to cool for 4-5 minutes before serving. Store any excess tightly covered in the refrigerator.

RANCH SALAD DRESSING

Terrific over salads or as a dip for veggies and cheeses.

Makes approximately 1 cup

¼ cup mayonnaise

¼ cup plain yogurt

½ cup lowfat buttermilk

Pinch of sea salt, (optional)

Pinch of pepper, white or black

¼ teaspoon celery seed

½ teaspoon minced garlic

1 teaspoon finely diced scallions (white bulb only)

1 teaspoon parsley

½ teaspoon chives

½ plus teaspoon dill

Thoroughly mix all ingredients and refrigerate for at least 2 hours, allowing the spices to blend. Store excess tightly covered in the refrigerator.

✧

CHEESE SAUCE

Goes great with fresh, steamed, or cooked veggies.

Makes approximately 1 cup

2 tablespoons canola or sunflower oil

1 tablespoons flour

1 cup warmed milk

¼ teaspoon garlic powder

⅓ cup shredded Cheddar, Colby, Swiss or Monterey Jack cheese

Dash of Tabasco®, hot sauce or lemon juice (optional)

Salt and pepper to taste

1. In a medium saucepan, whisk the oil and flour together until all lumps are broken up and the mixture begins to thicken.

2. Heat the flour mixture over medium heat while gradually adding the cheese and milk.

3. Stir this sauce constantly until it begins to thicken, and then allow sauce to simmer for 1-2 more minutes, stirring it a couple times to prevent burning.

4. As the sauce thickens, stir in the spices and then allow all to blend for about 20-30 seconds.

5. Remove the saucepan from the heat and distribute individual servings or pour the sauce over the main dish and serve. Store any excess cheese sauce tightly covered in the refrigerator. This sauce does not freeze well.

French Fries

How many times has the enticing, greasy scent of French Fries caused you to pull into the parking lot of a fast food restaurant? Gosh, they smell so good, don't they? Sure they do, but don't give in to the greasy temptation; instead, drive right on by. Then, once home make your own; as homemade fries are just as tempting and delicious as those that are massively produced, they just aren't prepared with an enormous amount of greasy fat.

✧

Preheat oven to 450° Fahrenheit	Serves 5-6

2 large potatoes

1-1½ tablespoons canola, sunflower or olive oil

½-1 teaspoon Sea salt

Seasoning of choice to taste: pepper, garlic salt, paprika, etc. (optional)

1 bowlful of ice cold water

1. Wash and peel the potatoes. Cut each into quarters, and then slice each quarter into ¼-½-inch thick sticks. Place the slices into the bowl of cold water while cutting the remaining slices to prevent browning.

2. Grease a cookie sheet with pan spray.

3. Thoroughly drain the water from the potatoes, then pour the potatoes onto a double layer of paper towels and pat them dry.

4. Spread the potato slices evenly onto the prepared pan and sprinkle the oil all over the slices. (You can also use an oil spray (not pan spray), now available at the grocery store in many locations.) Shake the pan to evenly distribute the oil all over the potatoes.

5. Place the potatoes in the oven and bake for 30-40 minutes or until golden brown and crisp. Make sure to flip the potatoes over 4-5 times while baking to ensure even browning

6. Remove the pan from the oven, turn the fries onto a paper towel lined plate or bowl, season with salt and seasoning, and serve immediately.

Sweet Potato/Yam Fries

Although many believe that yams and sweet potatoes taste the same, there is a true difference. Yams contain more natural sugar than sweet potatoes, and have much more moisture. However, both are wonderful in taste and are actually much healthier than your basic potato. Thus, for a terrific change of pace, make a batch of these once in a while and watch your family's appreciation as the last fry cheerfully disappears down the hatch into the bellies of those you love

✧

Preheat oven to 450° Fahrenheit   **Serves 4**

---

2 yams or sweet potatoes

1 teaspoon canola, sunflower, or olive oil

Sea salt, pepper, garlic powder to taste Dash of paprika (optional)

1. Grease a cookie sheet with pan spray.

2. Thoroughly wash and peel the potatoes. Then quarter and slice them into ¼-½-inch thick sticks and place them into a bowl.

3. Add the oil and seasonings to the potatoes and gently mix all together.

4. Evenly spread the potato slices all over the prepared pan. Bake for 30-40 minutes or until golden brown, flipping the potatoes over once or twice for even browning.

5. Remove the pan from the oven and serve the fries immediately.

✧ ✧ ✧

VARIATION

✧ For a little variety, these are also very good when mixed with cinnamon and Sea salt. To do so, mix 1 teaspoon of cinnamon with 2 pinches of Sea salt and proceed accordingly.

Potato Salad

More often than not, prepackaged potato salads are saturated in mayonnaise, and contain minimal vegetables. They sure are easy and relatively inexpensive, but not very nutritious. Yet when you make your own, you get the opportunity to relish in the magnificence of mingling flavors offered from a fine diversity of fresh, healthful ingredients.

✧

Serves 6-8

5 large russet potatoes, washed, peeled, and cut into 1-1½ inch chunks

5 large hard boiled eggs, peeled

¾ cup celery, diced

¾ cup red onion, diced

1-2 teaspoons minced garlic or 2 garlic cloves coarsely diced

2 teaspoons dill

½ teaspoon celery salt

Salt and pepper to taste

⅓ cup mayonnaise

3 tablespoons plain yogurt

Sprinkling of paprika for the top (optional)

1. Fill a large pot with warm water and bring the water to a full boil over medium-high heat.

2. Place the potatoes into the boiling pot of water and boil them until tender and easily pierced (approximately 15-20 minutes).

3. Drain the potatoes in a colander and then rinse them thoroughly with very cold water.

4. Place the potatoes into a large bowl.

5. Cut the peeled eggs into small chunks and then add them to the potatoes along with all the other ingredients, except the paprika.

6. Stir all the ingredients gently together with a rubber spatula or wooden spoon. While stirring the ingredients I recommend that you break up only a few of the larger potato chunks for a creamier texture, but leave the majority of the potatoes in chunks.

7. Sprinkle the top of the potato salad with a dash of paprika if you'd like and then cover it with plastic wrap and refrigerate the salad for at least an hour for best flavor.

Creamy Pasta Salad

The next time you are about to purchase a previously prepared, creamy pasta salad at the grocery, keep in mind that many are loaded with excess mayonnaise to increase the bulk weight of the product. Therefore, the next time you are tempted by the immediate gratification of creaminess and ease, just walk on by and right back to the produce aisle. Once there, fill your basket with fresh ingredients, and then smile in the checkout lane, for you made a healthier choice for your family today.

✦

Serves 6-8 as a meal or 16 as a side dish

One, 16 ounce box/bag rotini, shell or macaroni pasta

2-3 celery ribs, finely diced

1 small red onion. finely diced

1 small cucumber, diced

½ red pepper and/or tomato, seeded and finely diced

¾ cup finely chopped broccoli

½ cup sliced black olives (optional)

4 hard-boiled eggs, peeled and coarsely chopped

⅓ cup mayonnaise

2-3 tablespoons plain yogurt

2-3 tablespoons milk

½ teaspoon minced garlic

Sea salt and pepper to taste

Couple drops of freshly squeezed lemon juice (optional)

1. Cook the pasta according to the package directions.

2. Once the pasta is ready, pour it into a colander to drain and rinse it with very cold water immediately to cool down its temperature.

3. Pour the pasta, and all remaining ingredients into a large bowl and then gently mix all ingredients together until thoroughly blended.

4. Cover the top of the bowl with plastic wrap, and refrigerate for at least 1 hour prior to serving for best flavor.

✧ ✧ ✧

✄ VARIATION ✄

✧ Eliminate the eggs, mayonnaise, yogurt and milk from this recipe and instead mix together: ⅓ cup olive oil, 1⅓ cups red wine vinegar, ½ teaspoon each of minced garlic, oregano, basil and mustard and a few drops of lemon juice. Gently mix these ingredients with the pasta and vegetables and refrigerate until serving. Serve with Parmesan, Romano or Feta cheese.

Paradise Pasta Salad

I make this recipe often and enjoy it as a whole meal, using the leftovers to snack on later in the week. Maybe it is the taste of fresh fruit mixed with flavor enhancing ingredients, or just the ease of this recipe that make it so good. Perfect for a BBQ, picnic at the park, or just as it is for a quick and healthful meal; this recipe promises to be requested and enjoyed for many years to come.

✧

Serves 3-4 as a meal or 6-7 as a side dish

2 cups rotini or wheel shaped pasta

2½ cups of your favorite mixed, chopped fresh fruits, (e.g. pineapple, peaches, nectarine, mango, papaya, star fruits, berries, and pitted sweet dark cherries)

½ cup raisins, dark and/or golden

3-4 tablespoons of chopped almonds, sunflower seed or pumpkin seeds

2 tablespoons of white, rice, or red wine vinegar

3 tablespoons olive oil

A pinch of nutmeg and/or cinnamon

¼ cup fresh finely chopped mint, chocolate mint or basil

3-4 cups shredded spinach or lettuce

1. Cook the pasta according to the package directions.

2. Once the pasta has completed boiling, pour it into a colander to drain and thoroughly rinse it with very cold water to immediately cool down its temperature.

3. Pour the pasta into a large bowl, and then gently stir in all remaining ingredients, except the spinach, with a rubber spatula or wooden spoon.

4. Tightly cover the bowl with plastic wrap, and refrigerate until serving.

5. Divide the shredded spinach evenly between serving plates or bowls and serve the salad on top of the spinach.

HINT

Mint and Chocolate Mint herbs can easily be grown in a sunny windowsill as well as in a small garden. Once the leaves are grown, simply snip the stem from the mass, pick the small leaves off and allow them to dry in a bowl. Once thoroughly dry, simply break the leaves into small pieces and store them in a jar with a tight fitting lid.

Yogurt Banana Splits

❦

When you are in need of a quick meal, this incredibly ambrosial and delightful recipe is a marvelous alternative to fast and prepackaged meals.

✧

TIP:

♥ *Semi sweet chocolate chips are a type of dark chocolate, filled with antioxidants, and nutrients such as iron and calcium, and vitamins A, B1, C, D, and E; which makes them good for you in minimal amounts.*

✧

Serves 4-6

1 quart (32 ounce container) vanilla yogurt

4 large bananas

1 pint fresh blueberries or 1¼ cup frozen and thawed blueberries (drain juice and use it for Fruity Cubes, page 63)

1 small can unsweetened crushed pineapple

⅓-½ cup Strawberry Sauce, previously prepared (see page 158)

¼ cup mini semi sweet chocolate chips

2 tablespoons chopped nuts (optional)

1 pitted sweet dark cherry per scoop (Use more if you'd like)

1. Slice each banana in half lengthwise and place 2 halves into each serving bowls, or fruit bowls (i.e. cantaloupe, papaya, mango, honeydew, or small watermelons); (see page 55) after the internal seeds are removed.

2. Place two ½ cup scoops of yogurt between the banana slices. (For young children, use a small ice cream scoop or large spoon to distribute 3-4 smaller yogurt mounds between halved banana slices)

3. Sprinkle the blueberries around the bananas, and then drizzle the top of one mound with a tablespoon or two of Strawberry sauce or melted strawberry preserves.

4. Scoop approximately 1 tablespoon of crushed pineapple on top of the other yogurt mound and then sprinkle each mound with mini chocolate chips and nuts.

5. Place a sweet, dark, pitted cherry on the top of each yogurt mound and serve immediately.

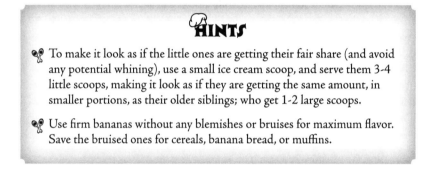

HINTS

- To make it look as if the little ones are getting their fair share (and avoid any potential whining), use a small ice cream scoop, and serve them 3-4 little scoops, making it look as if they are getting the same amount, in smaller portions, as their older siblings; who get 1-2 large scoops.

- Use firm bananas without any blemishes or bruises for maximum flavor. Save the bruised ones for cereals, banana bread, or muffins.

Strawberry Sauce

Scrumptiously delicious!

✧

Makes approximately 1½ cups, 2 tablespoons per serving.

---

1 quart fresh strawberries, stems removed and sliced into ½-inch thick pieces

⅓ cup cold water

⅓ cup sugar

1½ -2 tablespoons water

1 tablespoon cornstarch

1 tablespoon vanilla

1. Put the ⅓ cup water and sugar into a saucepan and bring to a boil over medium high heat. Let this mixture boil for 4-6 minutes, stirring occasionally to prevent browning.

2. Mix the cornstarch into the remaining water and stir until the cornstarch completely dissolves. Slowly whisk the cornstarch into the boiling water. Bring the mixture back to a boil and allow the sauce to boil for 2-3 more minutes.

3. Remove the pan from the heat and gently fold the strawberries and vanilla into the syrup. Serve immediately or refrigerate the syrup until it cools. This can be stored tightly covered in the refrigerator for up to 3 days.

HINT

Although, Strawberry Sauce pairs splendidly with sundaes, as well as when added to fruit salads to accentuate the flavor, there is an easy substitution for it when time is limited. Simply heat ⅓ cup of strawberry preserves in a saucepan or in the microwave for a minute or so until it melts, and then pour 1-2 tablespoons over each serving of yogurt or fruits.

Rules, Food and Consistency: **Stand Tall**

❧

"**R**ules, rules, rules!" "Oh no, not more rules, pretty please?" "Oh, come on mom and dad, no more rules!" "Oh dude!"

Well, mom and dad, as much as I hate to say this, you'll need to establish some food-related rules for your kids to ensure their health and quality of life. Will this be difficult? Not really! The hard part will be following through and being consistent when imposing them.

Rules provide structure and security. Although your kids may not know it, they welcome structure and rules, for they provide a sense of safety and security. Plus, rules do teach them how to take responsibility for their own actions.

My past experiences with helping and teaching children have taught me that whenever they are a part of making rules and associated consequences that directly affect them, they really do tend to respect them, and follow through more consistently. Therefore, it is essential for you to listen to and respect their input on such important issues. Setting a predetermined time, such as over a family meal or meeting, offers the opportunity for everyone to contribute and understand what are fair and realistic rules, and what the consequences will be if and when these rules are broken.

Another point to remember is that, for some rules, if they're good for one, then they're probably good for all. If you set a rule whereby food and beverages are not allowed near the computer, then you too must follow this same rule. Remember, you are their primary role model, so your rules should not be *"do as I say, not as I do,"* but *"do as I do!"*

Also please be aware, that being a 'softy' or too flexible when it comes to following through on set rules and associated consequences, can backfire on you. Sometimes being soft is easier than being firm, especially when those big eyes begin to plead and beg. Usually when an adult (parent, teacher, grandparent) gives in too often, or is too soft and forgiving, the result is that the kids learn that they can walk all over and around you. Sure, kids will be kids, and sometimes they may need a reminder, so give them a warning. If the rule continues to be broken, then they must deal with the preset consequences that will follow. Overall rules really do help to build confidence in children and instill in them a sense of taking responsibility for their own actions.

Keep in mind that any new rules and expectations do apply to your stubborn and/or bullying teenagers too. Do not be intimidated by a teen just because they may tower over you. Remind them that as their parent, you do know what is best for them, even if they disagree. Stand tall if you must and remind them that while they live under your roof, you make the final rules, while also providing for many of their needs! Do not give in to a bullying teenager just because they want to do this or have that extra helping of pie. Just as you won't allow them to stick their fingers into an electrical socket, when your child is overweight you won't allow them to devour lots of junky foods and over eat on a regular basis, while sitting around doing nothing. As long as your rules are realistic and fair, and the available foods/beverages taste good, they will adjust, as they have no other choice.

Examples of a few food-related rules

+ No food allowed in bedrooms.

+ No food is allowed outside of the kitchen and/or dining room, such as in the living room, den or garage, unless permission is previously granted.

+ No more than 1 type of baked treat per day. For instance, if they have cookies with lunch, then they may not have more cookies, cake or sweet breads (mini breads or muffins) as a snack after school or later in the evening.

+ Remind the kids that they must first ask permission for a snack between meals or late at night, as the kitchen is not their personal restaurant. Also, if their choice of a snack is not very healthful, offer them a couple alternatives. If they do not want the suggested alternative, then they have made their choice, to not have a snack.

+ They may not prepare their own food prior to asking permission. However, if such preparations are made to surprise you with, then adjust what you had planned and don't be too harsh on them for the resulting mess.

BREADS AND SWEETS

Breads and Sweets

Bread was one of the first foods baked all naturally from scratch, and then broken and shared among family and friends. At times they were the only source of food available. Candy was once a delicacy, as just 1 small piece was considered a precious gift to anyone; but especially to child, who would savor its sweet flavor for as long as he/she could. And cakes have been around since the Medieval Times; as the first cakes were similar to bread, but prepared with a sweeter essence provided by adding honey, nuts and dried fruits for flavor. In fact, ancient Europeans baked fruitcakes and gingerbreads often, because they would last for many months and help to feed their families during times of deprivation and famine.

Yet that was a long time ago. In many of today's modern societies these foods (breads and cakes) no longer sustain life; instead, when massively consumed that can and most likely will negatively affect our health, especially that of a child. Sure, whole grains help to promote energy, and a diet that is enriched by tasty whole grains does help protect our bodies from developing diabetes and heart diseases. Yet, when kids overeat these foods daily, and do not burn off the calories by being active, they can easily pack on excess weight, which could eventually be detrimental to their health and quality of life.

So how are you to cut back on how much bread, cake and, candy your kids are consuming? Well, initially you eliminate having too much easily available. Whole grain breads are indeed healthy, but do you honestly need several varieties (loaf bread, bagels, rolls, biscuits, crescents, tortillas and crackers) available in your home at all times? One or two of these varieties is a sufficient amount, especially when inducing weight loss and avoiding raising potentially obese kids. Also, eliminating any type of bread with dinner is a great beginning toward decreasing the amount of daily intake. If you're serving a dish that requires bread or a tortilla in the recipe, then eliminate the bread from another meal for that day. Likewise, when whole grain cereals are served for breakfast, then there is no need to serve toast, especially when an energizing piece of fresh fruit will better prepare them for the morning ahead.

Because kids will be kids, and sweets such as candy, cakes and cookies are a part of being a kid, the best way to control the amount of sweet treats that your children devour is to refrain from buying those prepackaged, fat inducing varieties, and prepare your own, all naturally from scratch. Know that eliminating all sweets from their daily diets is not a good idea, as it can induce hoarding and binging on such outside of the home. Yet, when you make your own scrumptious varieties, it's easier to control the amount available and reduce the temptation to hoard. Homemade foods make memories, while providing skills for self-sufficiency. Previously manufactured and packaged varieties only use up excess funds and get eaten. By the way, because the price of sugar is constantly on the rise, homemade varieties ultimately will cost less in dollars and body mass, than those previously prepared and packaged by a manufacturer. Additionally, when you prepare a large batch of sweets and breads, usually the excess can be frozen and served at another time. Most prepackaged varieties do not freeze very well.

"Oh no, more cooking and baking, when, how?" you might be asking yourself. Before you get distressed, look at it this way. These types of changes in daily eating habits are a positive and may cause everyone in your household to be happier as well as loose a few excess pounds; thus they are made for the benefit of all, not just one of your kids. Plus, when you allow a manufacturer to know what is best for your family's health and wellness, then there could be trouble knocking at your back door. Manufacturers are in the business of selling, not raising healthy kids. Nor do they add the most important ingredient of all into their manufactured offerings. You see, when you prepare your own foods, although they may take an extra dose of effort and energy, you get to add an extra scoop of love into each and every spin of the beater. After all, love is the most important ingredient of them all, and the only justified ingredient of which extra amounts can generously be added to induce more flavor.

Making better food decisions is not difficult, but it does take your participating effort. Though easier, many prepackaged sweets do not provide sustenance; instead they can pack on unhealthy excess pounds. So put them back on the shelf or steer your grocery cart right past that stocked aisle of cookies, cakes and candies and do not stop for doughnuts on the way home! Instead read the labels, purchase more healthful choices of bread and prepare your own homemade, delectable sweets. And get your kids to help you prepare these edible wonders for life, for lessons shared and learned in the kitchen are precious and will last for years to come.

Loaf Breads

When choosing breads at your local grocery store, don't forget to read the label before purchasing. If your choice of packaged bread does not have "whole" wheat or semolina flour listed as the first ingredient, then put it back on the shelf and choose a different, more healthful variety. Although most baked products are also prepared with bleached or unbleached white wheat flour, the following breads are the best choices you can make for both flavor and health.

✧

Whole Wheat Bread

Whole Wheat Tortillas and Rolls

Oat or Oat Nut Bread and Rolls

Rye Bread

Dark Rye Bread (Pumpernickel)

Multi-Grain Breads

Semolina Breads

Wheat, Blueberry, Raisin, Onion, Garlic or Seeded Bagels

HINT

🍴 When baking Gluten-free, substitute each cup of flour with ¾ cup plus 2 tablespoons of buckwheat flour, plus 2 tablespoons of Quinoa. Buckwheat is gluten-free; the only wheat it contains is in the title.

Oat Bread

The best part about this recipe is that it easy and provides for 2 loaves, one for the freezer and one now. As splendid for sandwiches as it is for toast, the good for you oats produce a natural woodsy flavor, and the texture is nicely soft and chewy, just as it should be.

✧

Makes 2 loaves

2 cups warm water

2 packages dry active yeast

¼ cup sugar

½ cup oats, quick or old fashioned

1 cup milk

1 tablespoon butter, melted

4½ -4¾ cups unbleached white flour

¼ cup (½ stick) butter

½ cup raisins, previously soaked in hot water, drained and patted dry (optional)

1 teaspoon cinnamon (optional)

2 teaspoons salt

Egg wash (1 egg white and 2 tablespoons water, mixed together)

HIGH ALTITUDE TIP Use 4¾ -5 cups of flour; allow the dough to rise in a humid spot if possible and place a pan filled with water onto the bottom oven rack when baking.

1. Sprinkle the yeast into a room temperature mixing bowl filled with ½ cup of the warm water. Stir the yeast into the water 1or 2 times, cover the bowl and then let it sit for 10 minutes or until it begins to bubble. Add the remaining water and sugar to the yeasty water and then allow all to dissolve for a few minutes.

2. While the yeast is dissolving, heat the milk to a boil, and then stir in the oats and melted butter. Constantly stir this mixture over medium heat for a little more than a minute, or until the oats have absorbed most of the milk. Allow the oats to cool until just warm.

HINT

- The dough should feel slightly warm when setting for the first period of rising.

3. In the mixing bowl, mix the ¼ cup of butter into the yeast mixture, while gradually adding the flours, oats, salt, and cinnamon and raisins (if using). Mix the dough until all ingredients are thoroughly incorporated.

4. Grease a different bowl with pan spray or butter.

5. Gather the dough together and place it into the greased bowl. Cover this bowl with a warm damp cloth. Place the dough in a warm area allowing it to rise until doubled in bulk, about 1 hour. (Do not place on a warm stove or heated clothes dryer to rise.)

6. Thoroughly grease two, 9x5-inch bread pans with pan spray or butter.

7. Once the dough has risen to double it's bulk, remove it from the bowl, divide it in half, and then knead each half a couple times on a lightly floured surface.

8. Shape each half into a loaf, and then fit each into the prepared pans. Cover each pan with a warm, damp cloth and allow the dough to rise till doubled in bulk again.

9. Preheat oven to 350° Fahrenheit.

10. Using a pastry brush or your fingers, brush the egg wash over the top of each loaf and then bake them for approximately 1 hour. You will know when the bread has completed baking when the top crust is golden and when you can gently tap the top of each loaf with your hand and hear a hollow sound from within.

11. Remove the pan from the oven, and spread a small amount of melted butter or canola-based butter spread all over the top of each loaf. Allow the breads to cool in the pan for approximately 10 minutes, and then remove them from the pans. It is best to allow each to cool thoroughly before slicing. Store the breads in a plastic bag or container or in a freezer-safe bag in the freezer.

Thee Alternative Wrap

When making better food decisions for your kids, a delicious habit to get into is replacing lunchtime sandwich breads with large, loose lettuce or spinach leaves. Once washed, these individual leaves make terrific, flavorful wraps when filled with a variety of deli meats, nutritious salads, and additional veggies. All you have to do is place the preferred fillings towards the top of the leaf, then fold the top of the leaf over the filling and begin to roll it as you would a jellyroll. These can be easily sealed with a small toothpick, and then placed into a sandwich bag or served immediately.

THE EGG SALAD WRAP

I am not sure what it is about this recipe, but it always sold out daily when I had the Bakery and Deli. Although the bakery's door is now closed, for some reason whenever I am ill, or in need of a light meal, this particularly easy recipe has always provided comfort; just as it did when my mom used to make it for me as a child.

Makes approximately 10 individual Lettuce Wraps or 4-5 servings

---

HINT

- The best leaves to use are red or green curly tipped leaves, butter or bib leaf lettuce, arugula leaves and of course, large spinach leaves. Your choice of leaf should be relatively loose from the center of the lettuce head and should not contain a thick inner vein, which would hamper the ability to roll it easily around various fillings.

10 large lettuce or spinach (stems removed) leaves, previously washed and patted dry with a paper towel

10 large hard-boiled eggs

1 cup celery, finely diced

1 cup red onions finely diced

5 level tablespoons mayonnaise

1-1 ½ teaspoons dill, (amount is of personal preference)

Sea salt and pepper to taste

Additions: 5 thin tomato and/or cucumbers slices-halved, sprouts, thinly sliced pickles, grated carrots, dark or golden raisins, chopped dried apricots and/or sunflower seeds

1. Crack and peel the shells from the eggs, and chop into small chunks.

2. Add remaining ingredients and mix until all ingredients are thoroughly incorporated.

3. Cover and refrigerate until serving or preparing the wraps.

4. To prepare the wraps, place 2-3 scant tablespoons of the salad about 1-inch below the top of each leaf. If using any of the additions, sprinkle or place them on top of the salad. Then fold the very top of the leaf over and under the salad and continue rolling the leaf over the filling. Seal each wrap with a small toothpick. (If some of the salad leaks out of the sides, scoop it up and place back into the bowl and refrain from rolling the wrap too tight.)

✧ ✧ ✧

✐ VARIATIONS ✑

✧ Substitute one 24-ounce water based can of Albacore Tuna Fish for the eggs; delete the sea salt from the recipe and add ½ teaspoon of minced garlic and a couple squeezes of fresh squeezed lemon juice instead. Make sure to drain all the juice from the tuna prior to mixing it with the other ingredients.

✧ Any assortment of thin sliced deli meats, cheeses, and veggies can be used when preparing these delicious wraps.

✧ Avocados can be added, just make sure that the slices are cut thin to prevent them from sliding out of the wrap.

Zip Itty Doo Dah Breads
(Mini Strawberry Breads)

Although these little treats may not bring bluebirds onto your family's shoulders, they will, nonetheless, bring plenty of sunshine to those you love. The best part about this fabulous recipe is that it makes a terrific snack, and when served as a lunch (boxed, bagged or at home), with a few slices of cheese and fresh fruits, everything will be satisfactual. Each and every bite produces a wonderful feeling, thus it may just get the kids to start coming your way in more ways than one.

✧

Preheat oven to 350° Fahrenheit	**Makes about 8 mini loaves**

½ cup butter, margarine or canola oil spread

¾ cup sugar

2 eggs

1 tablespoon vanilla

⅔ cup plain yogurt

1¾ cups flour

½ teaspoon baking soda

½ teaspoon baking powder

¼ teaspoon cinnamon

1¼ cup fresh sliced strawberries

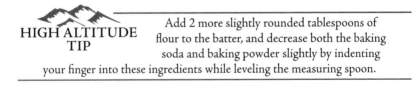

HIGH ALTITUDE TIP Add 2 more slightly rounded tablespoons of flour to the batter, and decrease both the baking soda and baking powder slightly by indenting your finger into these ingredients while leveling the measuring spoon.

1. Thoroughly grease an 8-section mini loaf pan with pan spray, butter or margarine.

2. In a mixing bowl, cream the butter and sugar, then add the eggs, yogurt and vanilla and mix thoroughly.

3. Add the remaining ingredients and continue mixing until all the ingredients are thoroughly incorporated.

4. Pour the batter evenly into each section of prepared pan and bake for about 17-20 minutes or until an inserted knife or toothpick comes out clean.

5. Remove the individual breads from the pan within a minute to prevent further baking, allow the steam to evaporate for another minute or so, and then wrap each individually in plastic wrap.

✧ ✧ ✧

VARIATIONS

✧ Of course you can use an 8x4-inch loaf pan. However, the baking time required will increase to about 50-60 minutes. Remember to always check a product for doneness by inserting a knife or toothpick into the center of the products. If it comes out clean or with only 1-2 crumbs attached, then it has completed baking.

✧ Blueberries, sweet dark cherries, pomegranates or huckleberries can be used in place of the strawberries.

Chini Weenie Spice Breads
(Zucchini Mini Breads)

As a confessed fussy eater, I would not eat many green colored foods growing up. My mom tried various veggie recipes, but still I would only eat lettuce and peas. Anything else that was green, I refused to eat, and it subtly went to our dog hiding under the table. However, whenever my grandmother prepared these scrumptious little treats, I would gobble them up without a second thought. Years later I found the recipe in her treasured recipe box, in an unfamiliar handwriting labeled "For Randi." I was flabbergasted when I saw that one of the main ingredients was *green*! Since sharing it in writing, many have made this savory recipe only to receive rave reviews from all, including their children.

✦

Preheat oven to 350° Fahrenheit   Makes 8-9 mini breads or large muffins

HINTS

- These are best served with a soup, salad or just as they are, as a snack. Keep in mind that this may be sweet, but still a bread recipe. Therefore, I suggest that you eliminate serving bread for lunch or breakfast on the same day that they are prepared.

- Feedback from many, including several pregnant nurses, has informed me that when this recipe is prepared with raisins, it helps to pass food more easily through the digestive system. Just remember to soak the raisins in hot water, prior to adding them to any type of food you are preparing.

- Add an extra egg when doubling and 2 extra eggs when tripling this recipe.

2 cups grated zucchini

1 cup canola or safflower oil

1 cup sugar

1 cup firmly packed brown sugar

⅓ cup molasses

2 tablespoons vanilla

3 eggs

3 cups flour

1 teaspoon baking soda

¼ teaspoon baking powder

1 tablespoon cinnamon

1 teaspoon nutmeg

½ teaspoon cloves

¾ cup of raisins, chopped dates, figs and/or chopped nuts, optional

HIGH ALTITUDE TIP Add 2 more slightly rounded tablespoons of flour to the batter, and decrease both the baking soda and baking powder slightly by indenting your finger into these ingredients while leveling the measuring spoon.

1. Thoroughly grease 8-9 mini bread or large muffin pan sections with pan spray or butter. (If using 2 pans, do not grease the additional empty sections; partially fill them with water instead.)

2. Mix together the oil, sugars, vanilla, eggs, molasses and zucchini.

3. Add the flour, baking soda, baking powder, spices and choice of raisins and/or walnuts to the sugar mixture. Mix all the ingredients at slow speed for 2 minutes to make sure that they are thoroughly incorporated into the batter. Once the ingredients are thoroughly mixed, stir it once or twice from the bottom up, using a rubber spatula, to ensure that all of the oil is mixed into the batter.

4. Fill each mini bread or muffin section to just below the top of each pan section with the batter.

5. Bake 25-35 minutes, or until toothpick comes out clean.

6. Once baking has completed, remove each individual loaf from the pan within a minute or 2 to prevent further baking. Allow the steam to evaporate for another minute or two. If serving fresh from the oven, it is best to allow these breads to cool for 10 minutes first for maximum flavor. To store, wrap each individually in plastic wrap. These will stay fresh for 2-3 days, or they can easily be frozen in a freezer-safe baggie and thawed for immediate satisfaction at another time. To thaw, simply place the desired amount of breads into the microwave and defrost for a minute or more until warm.

The Best Banana Bread

To be totally honest, I was not going to add this bread recipe, as there are numerous recipes available for Banana Bread and you may even have a favorite of your own. However, because I have continuously received compliments stating that this one of the best banana breads ever tasted, I felt that it must be shared. I admit, it is quite moist, relatively healthy and perfectly scrumptious.

✧

Preheat oven to 350° Fahrenheit	7-8 servings per loaf

5 large, ripe bananas or 6 small bananas

½ cup (1 stick) of butter or margarine

½ cup sugar

2 eggs

1¼ cups flour

¾ teaspoon baking soda

1 teaspoon baking powder

1 tablespoon cinnamon

¾ cup raisins, chopped walnuts, blueberries, pomegranates and/or semi-sweet chocolate chips may be added

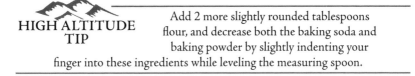

HIGH ALTITUDE TIP Add 2 more slightly rounded tablespoons flour, and decrease both the baking soda and baking powder by slightly indenting your finger into these ingredients while leveling the measuring spoon.

1. Mash the bananas in the mixing bowl.

2. Add the butter, sugar and eggs to the bananas, and then cream these ingredients thoroughly together.

3. Add all of the remaining ingredients to the egg mixture and then at slow speed, mix the batter until all ingredients are thoroughly incorporated. (Do not over mix the batter!)

4. Thoroughly grease a 9x5-inch bread pan with pan spray or butter.

5. Pour the batter evenly into the prepared pan.

6. Bake 55-65 minutes or until inserted knife comes out clean.

HINT

A slice of this fruit-filled bread is a splendid, tasty alternative for pretzels, chips or cookies after school.

7. Remove the bread from the pan within a minute after removing it from the oven to prevent further baking. Allow then steam to evaporate for a minute or 3 and then wrap the bread in plastic wrap. This bread is best sliced when cool to prevent breakage.

Copper Pennies
(Mini Apple Muffins)

These divine little treats are filled with fiber, antioxidants and lots of comforting, sweet flavor. I fondly remember eating lots of these delights when I was a kid. I thought they were some kind of homemade candy until decades later when I found the recipe in my grandmom's old box of recipe treasures. I discovered that they are mini muffins that just never developed much height.

✧

TIP:

💜 *It is common knowledge that whole apples help keep teeth and gums clean, but any form of the apple also helps to battle high cholesterol levels, while keeping our digestive systems healthy. Yet an interesting, fun fact to teach your kid is that apples, as well as peaches, plums, apricots, pears, strawberries, blackberries, raspberries and cherries, are all members of the Rose Family. Just as these common fruits are produced from a flower's central pistil, and protected by five equal leaves, so are rosehip berries, which are produced by a grand variety of wild roses.*

✧

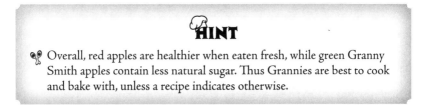

HINT

Overall, red apples are healthier when eaten fresh, while green Granny Smith apples contain less natural sugar. Thus Grannies are best to cook and bake with, unless a recipe indicates otherwise.

Preheat oven to 350° Fahrenheit	6-8 per serving

½ cup sugar

½ cup canola (or sunflower) oil

2 eggs

1 tablespoon vanilla

1 tablespoon lemon juice

1 teaspoon lemon peel

2 cups plus 2 tablespoons grated Granny Smith apples

1⅓ cups flour

1 teaspoon baking soda

2 teaspoons cinnamon

½ teaspoon each of nutmeg and cloves

¾ cup of chopped pecans or raisins (optional)

HIGH ALTITUDE TIP

Add an extra egg when doubling or 2 extra eggs when tripling this recipe, and decrease the baking soda slightly by indenting your finger into the ingredient while leveling the measuring spoon.

1. Thoroughly mix the sugar, oil, eggs, vanilla, lemon juice and lemon peel.

2. Add the flour, baking soda, raisins and/or pecans, alternately, with the grated apples to the sugar mixture. Thoroughly mix the batter.

3. Thoroughly grease 2 dozen mini muffin pan sections with pan spray or butter.

4. Fill each muffin section to the top with the batter, and if using pecans sprinkle some chopped nuts on top of each muffin.

5. Bake 14-35 minutes (depending on size of the muffin section) or until inserted toothpick comes out clean.

6. Remove the muffins from the pan within a minute after removing from the oven. These can be wrapped in clear plastic film or stored in a plastic baggie once cool.

Honey Bunch Cake

This marvelous little cake is an offering of the heavenly delight of homemade goodness at best. Oh my, the fragrance alone can make your kids salivate in anticipation. And, it tastes so good, that it may also get your little honeybunches momentarily away from the TV and into the kitchen to help with the clean up and share a few extra kisses in exchange for the first sensational slice.

Preheat oven to 375° Fahrenheit	**6-8 servings**

3 large Granny Smith apples or Bartlett pears

¼ cup honey, set aside.

1 cup

1½ teaspoons baking powder

Pinch of salt

2 tablespoons butter

2 tablespoons honey

2 large egg yolks, beaten

½ cup milk

½ teaspoon nutmeg and/or cinnamon

1 teaspoon lemon or orange zest

HIGH ALTITUDE TIP

Add an additional slightly round tablespoon of flour, and decrease the baking powder slightly by indenting your finger into the ingredient while leveling the measuring spoon.

1. Thoroughly grease a 9-inch round pan with a removable bottom with pan spray.

2. Peel, pit and slice the choice of fruit into ⅛-¼ inch slices. Set fruit slices aside in a separate bowl. Cover the fruit filled bowl with a paper towel.

3. Mix together the flour, baking powder, salt, butter, 2 tablespoons honey, egg yolks and milk. Thoroughly mix the ingredients until fully incorporated.

4. Spread the dough all over the bottom and sides of the prepared pan. (The edge of the dough will over hang the pan about an inch or more. Do not trim this extra dough.)

5. Place the chosen fruit in the dough with cut side down.

> **HINT**
>
> ❧ If you do not have a removable bottom pan, a 9-inch round cake pan will work fine; but you will be unable to remove the cake from the pan.

6. Pour the reserved ¼ cup honey over the top of the fruit, and then sprinkle ½ teaspoon nutmeg and/or cinnamon over the honey.

7. Sprinkle 1 teaspoon of orange peel or zest over the spices.

8. Gently fold the extra dough over the apples, so that it covers about 1¼ inches of the apples.

9. Bake 30-40 minutes. Test this cake for doneness by inserting a toothpick or knife into the center of the cake after 30 minutes. If it comes out clean, then the cake has completed baking. Remove it from the oven, allow it to set for 2-3 minutes and then remove the outer pan shell, by pressing the removable bottom with a potholder up and out of the pan shell. Serve warm for best flavor. For a special treat serve warm with frozen vanilla or cinnamon yogurt.

Choc-n-gurt Cake

What does a baseball batter do when he wants to win the game by surprising the pitcher? He bunt hits the ball! So as a parent what can you do to surprise your family, and win the blessing of smiles? You bundt a wonderfully delicious cake!

✧

TIPS:

♥ *A small amount of butter is not as bad for you as many may think. In fact, butter is filled with vitamin A, D, E and K, as well as antioxidants. Butter helps to prevent tooth decay, and is also a potent source for building muscles and improving our immunity systems.*

♥ *Although not to be served daily, homemade cakes are much healthier than those previously prepared and packaged. Most prepackaged cakes have extra chemicals and ingredients added to lengthen their shelf life. At least homemade varieties are prepared from fresh ingredients!*

✧

Preheat oven to 350° Fahrenheit   **Serves 8**

¾ cup (1½ sticks) butter

1⅔ cups sugar

2 large eggs

1 tablespoon vanilla

1 cup plain yogurt

2 cups flour

¾ cup cocoa

2 teaspoons baking soda

1 cup buttermilk

1 cup (6-ounces) mini semi-sweet chocolate chips (larger chips will sink to the bottom of the cake) or finely chopped peanut butter chips

3 cups fresh stemmed strawberries, raspberries, blackberries or stemmed and pitted sweet dark cherries (optional)

2 teaspoons powdered sugar (optional)

HIGH ALTITUDE TIP Add 2 slightly rounded tablespoons flour, and 1 extra tablespoon of both buttermilk and yogurt to the recipe. Additionally, decrease the baking soda slightly by indenting your finger into the ingredient while leveling the measuring spoon.

1. Cream together the butter, sugar, eggs and vanilla.

2. Add the yogurt to the butter mixture and mix.

3. Add the flour, cocoa and baking soda to the butter mixture alternately with the buttermilk.

4. Add the mini chocolate chips to the batter as the last ingredient, and then mix all the ingredients together until thoroughly incorporated.

5. Thoroughly grease a bundt pan with pan spray or butter and then lightly flour the pan.

6. Pour the batter evenly into the prepared pan.

7. Bake 45-50 minutes or until an inserted knife or toothpick comes out clean.

8. Allow the cake to set in the pan for about 2 minutes and then invert it onto a serving plate and then and then very gently, invert the cake back to topside up. (Large spatulas are suggested to use when re-inverting the cake to topside up.) Allow the cake to set for another 2-4 minutes and then cover it with plastic wrap until serving. Once the cake has cooled, and just before serving it, fill the center hole with the fruit, and then sprinkle the top with the powdered sugar, if desired.

9. Thoroughly wrap the leftovers in plastic wrap, or wrap and then freeze the remaining cake in a freezer-safe baggie.

Bumbles Cake

I mistakenly came up with this cake while preparing a Streusel Cake developed over 100 years ago by my Great Grandmother. What can I say; I was in a hurry and somehow forgot about adding the middle layer of streusel. Although, the center streusel was absent, those who were fortunate to get a taste, found this bumbled cake to still be *"irresistibly dee-licious."*

✧

Preheat oven to 350° Fahrenheit	12 servings

Topping and Filling

1¼ cups packed brown sugar   2 tablespoons cinnamon

¼ cup (½ stick) butter

Mix these 3 ingredients together to make the streusel, and then set it aside in a small bowl.

HINT

Because this cake is large, I suggest cutting it in half crosswise, and removing half of the cake from the pan with a large spatula. Once this half is removed from the pan, wrap it thoroughly in plastic wrap and then freeze it in a freezer-safe bag for your family's enjoyment at another time.

Cake

1 cup (2 sticks) butter

1⅓ cups sugar

6 eggs

3 cups flour

2 teaspoons baking powder

2 teaspoon baking soda

2 cups plain yogurt

HIGH ALTITUDE TIP Add 2-3 slightly rounded tablespoons of flour to the recipe, and decrease both the baking soda and baking powder slightly by indenting your finger into these ingredients while leveling the measuring spoon.

1. Cream together the butter, sugar and eggs.

2. Add the flour, yogurt, baking powder and baking soda to the butter mixture. Mix the batter until all ingredients are thoroughly incorporated.

3. Thoroughly grease a 9x13-inch pan with pan spray or butter.

4. Spread the batter evenly into the prepared pan.

5. Sprinkle the streusel evenly all over the top of the batter and then bake the cake for 45-55 minutes or until an inserted knife or toothpick comes out clean.

6. Allow the steam to evaporate and then cover the cake, in the pan, with plastic wrap. Let cool for at least an hour for best flavor.

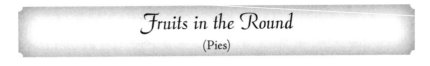

Fruits in the Round
(Pies)

Although there are numerous prepackaged fruit filled pies and pie fillings available, including at restaurants, nothing will ever taste as good as your homemade, love-filled pies. The best part about making your own varieties is that you can pile up the fruits and eliminate lots of excess sugar commonly added to other varieties, including those found in a can. It would not be proper for me to give the secrets related to prepackaged and store bought pie fillings, therefore you must trust me when I inform you that homemade pies are much healthier and flavorful than those pies and fillings previously prepared.

✧

7-8 servings

Lattice Topped Crust

Because a fruit pie's crust is usually the most fattening part of a pie, it is suggested to roll the dough out to as thin as you can and still handle it and either discard the excess dough or make Cinnamon Twists as directed below the pie recipe (page 186) and then store them for another day's treats.

2 cups flour	¼ cup water
1 teaspoon salt	¾ plus 1 tablespoon shortening

1. Sift together the flour and salt.
2. Add the water to ¼ cup of the flour/salt combination and mix to make a paste.
3. With a pastry blender or two forks, cut the shortening into the remaining flour until crumbly and little beads begin to form.

4. Pour every last bit of the paste into the flour/shortening mixture and with a fork work the paste into the mixture until manageable.

5. Form the dough into 2 flat balls and then roll each out onto a floured surface until thin and easy to handle.

6. Fit one of the round dough disks into a previously greased pie pan.

7. Prepare the top crust by placing the remaining ball of dough onto waxed paper, roll the dough until thin and then slice 10-14, half inch wide strips for a lighter lattice top and set aside on the same piece of waxed paper (You will only use 10 of the strips, but for best effect cut the dough slices into ½-inch wide slices, not wider.)

Fruit Pie Filling

Preheat oven to 375° Fahrenheit

6 cups or more of fresh or fresh frozen sweet dark pitted cherries, berries, peaches, plums and/or apricots

¼ -⅓ cup sugar or sugar substitute (Use the larger amount for tart fruits, i.e. raspberries)

2½ tablespoons tapioca

½ teaspoon vanilla

1 teaspoons freshly squeezed lemon juice

1 tablespoon milk

1. If using frozen fruit, thaw the fruits in the microwave for a few minutes until the fruits just begin to develop a small amount of juice. Firm, partially thawed fruits work best, as they will thaw completely while mixing in the other ingredients and baking.

2. Gently toss all of the filling ingredients together in a large

HINT

❦ If using berries, add ½ teaspoon cinnamon to the fruit mixture; if using peaches, plums or apricots add ½ teaspoon of nutmeg to the fruits and if using cherries add ½ teaspoon of almond extract to the fruit prior to pouring the filling into the prepared crust.

Fruit Pie continued on next page

Fruit Pie continued

bowl, prepare the crust (pg. 184), and then pour the filling into the prepared pie pan.

3. Once the pie shell is filled, begin applying the lattice topping by laying 5 strips of dough strips vertically on top of the fruit. Then set the other 5 strips of dough horizontally across the other strips. For a pretty effect, it is suggested to gently weave the horizontal strip alternately over and under the vertical strips.

4. Using a pasty brush or your fingers, brush the top of the pie with a tablespoon of milk.

5. Bake for about 45-50 minutes or until juices begin to bubble. If the pie edge begins to brown, cover the edge with a piece of foil and continue baking. Allow cooling for 30 or more minutes prior to serving for maximum flavor.

✧

PIE DOUGH CINNAMON TWISTS

1. Gather together all of the remaining pie dough, and then roll it out again, until thin.

2. Slice the remaining pie dough into ½ inch wide slices.

3. Spread each strip with a small amount of canola-based butter spread and then cut each strip in half width wise.

4. Sprinkle cinnamon sugar lightly over the top of each piece, and then, very gently, twist each strip twice by holding each edge and twisting the dough.

5. Bake the twists until golden, but not browned (about 7-9 minutes), at 375° Fahrenheit and then once cool, store them in a lined tin can to maintain crispness.

Cheesy Crème Strudelidoo

A perfectly scrumptious delight!

✧

Preheat oven to 375° Fahrenheit   **Serves 6-8**

½ package puff pastry sheet, partially thawed

12 ounces (1½ 8oz. blocks) Neufchatel or low fat cream cheese

¼ cup honey, agave nectar or sugar substitute

1 tablespoon vanilla

1¼ cups fresh berries, sliced strawberries, diced peaches, diced apricots, sweet dark pitted cherries-halved or pomegranate seeds

1. Spray a large cookie sheet with pan spray.

2. Place the partially thawed puff pastry sheet in the center of the prepared pan and roll it out a little bit on each side. (If the center creases appear thin, pinch the creases together before rolling.)

3. Spreading the filling within an inch or more from of each edge of the puff pastry sheet.

4. Place a row or two rows (for smaller fruits) of fruit at the top of the filling, in the center of the filling and about an inch from the end of the filling. (Do not overlap the fruits.)

5. Begin to roll the dough and filling up as a jellyroll, pinching or tucking in the side edges as you roll to prevent leaking. Roll the strudel up 3 times, and at the last roll, very gently bring the remaining dough up and over the top and begin to pinch it in the base of the dough to seal the ingredients in. (Make sure that this seam is thoroughly sealed, by pinching the dough together every ¼ inch or less.)

6. Once sealed, roll the dough back over to topside up, brush the top with an egg wash (1 egg mixed with 2 tablespoon of water) or milk, and then cut three shallow slits on the top of the dough. If you'd like, you can sprinkle a handful of chopped nuts on the top of the strudel just before baking it for 40-45 minutes or until it is golden and crisp.

7. Allow complete cooling before serving. Cover the leftovers in plastic wrap and store in the refrigerator for up to 2 more days.

Cheesy Crème Cups

Often described as "totally awesome," this yummy recipe will definitely become a family favorite and is much healthier than a prepackaged candy bar, cake or cookie as a snack. For a special treat, not only is this recipe as light and dreamy as a cloud, it's amazingly easy to prepare. So bring the kids into the kitchen to help and enjoy the good times' together while you still can.

✧

Preheat oven to 375° Fahrenheit

You will need 12 regular-sized muffin pan sections or 46-48 mini muffin pan sections

½ package puff pastry sheet, partially thawed

12 ounces (1½ 8oz. blocks) Neufchatel or low fat cream cheese

¼ cup honey, agave nectar or sugar substitute

1 tablespoon vanilla

1-2 tablespoons milk

A variety of fresh berries, sliced strawberries, sweet dark pitted cherries-halved or pomegranate seeds.

1. Thoroughly grease all muffin sections in your choice of pan with pan spray.

2. Mix the cream cheese, honey, vanilla and milk thoroughly together until thick, smooth and creamy.

3. Gently open the puff pastry sheet and then proceed to cut 12 or 48 small squares into the dough with a serrated knife.

4. Working quickly so as not to ruin the dough, gently stretch and pull each square and fit it into each prepared pan section. (If the dough breaks, simply mesh it back together by rubbing the seams together with your fingers. Also, know that each pastry square needs only to cover the bottom and partially up the sides of each muffin pan section.)

5. Fill each prepared section with the filling. If there is excess filling divide it evenly between the sections. Top each with a piece of fruit.

6. Bake the large puffs for about 20-25 minutes or until firm and the crust is golden, or the mini puff for about 12-15 minutes.

✧ ✧ ✧

VARIATION

✧ If you don't have time to mess with individual puffs, make a Strudel.

Golden, Dark and Fruity Puddings

Kids adore the soothing nature of puddings. But are those prepackaged, artificially flavored and colored varieties the best choice when making better food choices? Homemade puddings are prepared with all natural ingredients, contain less sugar and fat and take about the same time to prepare as those prepared from a box.

✦

HINTS

- When your kids are overweight, although easy, the individual prepackaged containers of pudding are not the best choice for them to snack on while sitting in school learning and studying. But after school or on weekends, a ½ cup of homemade pudding offers the same soft, comforting bliss, just without the excess sugar, fat and artificial coloring or flavors added for appeal.

- If you do not have individual ramekins or pudding cups available, used and previously cleaned, individual yogurt containers are wonderful to store the following pudding recipes in. To cover, just use a small piece of plastic wrap.

- If you'd prefer to make a 'special occasion' treat such as a Banana Crème Pie, simply prepare and bake a pie crust (see page 184) in a 9-inch pie pan, and then once cool, thinly slice 3 bananas on top of the previously baked and cooled crust. Pour the hot pudding on top of the bananas and allow the pie to cool for 30-45 minutes prior to placing it in the refrigerator until serving. Make sure the pie is completely chilled before serving.

- No, a whipped cream topping is not necessary to enjoy the great flavor of this Pudding Pie.

VANILLA PUDDING

Approximately eight, ½ cup servings

¼ cup cornstarch

½ cup sugar

4 egg yolks, slightly beaten

2½ cups milk

1½ tablespoons vanilla

2½ tablespoons butter

Sliced bananas, berries, sweet dark cherries slices, diced peaches, plums or apricots.

1. Thoroughly mix together the sugar and cornstarch in a medium sized saucepan.

2. Add the milk, vanilla and eggs to the sugar and then mix the ingredients together with a rubber spatula, making sure all sugar is incorporated and not lying on the bottom of the pan. Add the butter last to the top of these ingredients, but do not mix it in.

3. Cook these ingredients over medium high heat, stirring constantly to prevent burning. After about 7-10 minutes, the mixture will begin to thicken. Continue stirring the pudding until it just begins to boil and then turn off the heat, remove the pan from the heat and continue stirring the pudding for 1 minute.

4. Immediately cover the pudding in the saucepan with a piece of plastic wrap to prevent a skin from forming.

5. Allow the pudding to cool for 30 minutes, while you prepare the fruit.

6. Just before the 30 minutes are up, add a tablespoon or so of the fruit to the bottom of a plastic container, individual ramekins. If using banana slices, add about 5-6 thin slices to the bottom of the preferred container.

7. Evenly distribute the pudding over the fruit, allow it to sit and cool for about 30-45 minutes and then refrigerate until serving.

✧ ✧ ✧

❧ VARIATIONS ❧

✧ **LEMON PUDDING:** Substitute the vanilla with pure lemon extract, and add 1 heaping tablespoon of Lemon Curd to the main ingredients. Then while removing the pan from the heat, add 2 tablespoons of fresh squeezed lemon juice to the pudding as you stir it for an additional minute. Make sure that the juice is at room temperature prior to adding. By the way. Lemon Pudding Pie with berries hidden under the creamy filling is sure to win the approval of all around your table. The only difference between the pudding and pie, is a that the berries and pudding are placed and poured on top of a previously baked crust in a 9-inch pie pan (see page 184), and allowed it to cool for about 30-45 prior to placing it in the refrigerator until serving. Make sure the pie is completely chilled before serving.

✧ **COCONUT CRÈME PUDDING:** Stir about ¼ cup unsweetened shredded coconut into the pudding just before removing it from the heat.

✧

DARK CHOCOLATE PUDDING

Approximately eight, ½ cup servings

3¼ squares of unsweetened chocolate

¾ cup plus 2 tablespoons sugar

¼ cup plus 1 tablespoon cornstarch

3 egg yolks

3 cups of milk

1 tablespoon vanilla

1. Melt the chocolate in a small microwave safe bowl for about 1-2 minutes, check, stir and give it another minute or so if necessary until the chocolate is thoroughly melted; and then set the melted chocolate aside.

2. In a medium saucepan completely mix together the sugar and cornstarch.

3. Add the milk, vanilla and eggs to the sugar and mix with a rubber spatula making sure all sugar is incorporated and not laying on bottom of the pan. Add the butter to the top of these ingredients.

4. Cook these ingredients over medium high heat, stirring consistently to prevent burning.

5. After about 7-10 minutes the mixture will begin to thicken. Just as it begins to boil, turn off the heat, remove the pan from the heat, and continue stirring for one minute.

6. Using a rubber spatula, add the melted chocolate to the filling and thorough-

ly mix it in until fully incorporated and the pudding turns a dark brown with no golden streaks remaining.

HINT: This is when this pudding tastes the best in my personal opinion.

7. You can either serve it immediately while hot or cover the pudding with a piece of plastic wrap to prevent a skin from forming.

8. Allow the pudding to cool for 30 minutes and then stir it once again prior to distributing it between individual ramekins or small plastic containers and refrigerate.

✧ ✧ ✧

VARIATION

✧ Add berries and/or diced or sliced fruits to the bottom of each container prior to filling with the pudding. Bananas, cherries or berries pair exceptionally well with this recipe.

Snappers

When I thought about another cookie for you to make, I couldn't resist the temptation of adding this full-flavored, mouth-watering, low fat recipe. Many people who have had the opportunity to taste them are in awe when they learn that yes, these cookies are lower in fat and still make a snapping sound when broken. In fact, a highly acclaimed culinary professional challenged my authority on this recipe. She just couldn't believe that a low fat gingersnap would still snap when broken. So I gave her the recipe and the next morning I received an e-mail message praising this cookie, as *"one of the best I ever tasted."*

✧

TIP:

💗 *As previously stated, ginger, is one of most beneficial spices humans can ingest. It is good for the belly, helps to eliminate inflammations, and can change a bad day into one that is bright and sunny, even while the rain continues to pound the pavements, hills, and valleys for another day.*

✧

Preheat oven to 325° Fahrenheit

Makes approximately 36-40 cookies depending on size.

Cinnamon Sugar Mixture

¾ cup sugar   1½-2 tablespoons cinnamon

Mix together and set aside in a small bowl.

1 cup canola, safflower or sunflower oil

1 cup sugar

½ cup plus 1 teaspoon brown sugar

2 eggs

⅓ cup molasses

2½ cups flour

2 teaspoons ginger

½ teaspoon nutmeg

½ teaspoon cloves

2 teaspoons cinnamon

2 teaspoons baking soda

Additions: raisins, craisins or nuts etc.

HIGH ALTITUDE TIP

Increase the flour by 1 slightly rounded tablespoon, and decrease the baking soda slightly by indenting your finger into these ingredients while leveling the measuring spoon.

1. Mix together the margarine, oil and sugars. Add the eggs and the molasses to the sugar mixture, and mix thoroughly.

2. Add the flour, baking soda, spices and choice of an addition to the mixture. Mix all ingredients together at slow speed until thoroughly incorporated. (Do not over beat the dough) This batter will be very moist.

3. Grease 2-3 cookie sheets

4. Lightly flour the palms of your hands. (Optional)

5. Use a tablespoon full of batter or simply scoop up a small amount of the dough with a finger, and then roll the dough into a ball with the palms of your hands.

6. Thoroughly coat each cookie in the cinnamon sugar by rolling it in the mixture, and then place each onto the prepared cookie sheets. Lightly flatten the top of each cookie with the palm of your hand.

7. Bake 12-14 minutes, or until the edges just begin to brown.

Mama Nature Bars

There is something about the natural scent and flavor of oats combined with cinnamon, nutmeg and fruit that say comfort and health with each bite. Maybe it is because these flavors pair so exquisitely well or because they illustrate the taste of natural goodness provided for by Mother Nature. Whatever it is that makes these combined flavors so appetizing doesn't really matter; for what matters is that these bars will fill your home with the scent of love, while each bite is packed with sustenance, sweetness, and outstanding flavor.

✧

Preheat oven to 375° Fahrenheit   **Makes 8-12 servings**
(Remember serving sizes will vary depending on age. Thus for convenience cut these bars into 8 pieces, and then cut 1 or 2 bars in half for your younger kids.)

1 cup flour	1 teaspoon cinnamon
1 cup brown sugar	½ teaspoon nutmeg
½ cup canola oil	2 cups Quick Oats
1 teaspoon vanilla	¾ cup raisins (previously soaked)
⅓ cup plain yogurt	and/or peeled and diced apples
½ teaspoon baking soda	

HIGH ALTITUDE TIP

Increase the flour by 1 slightly rounded tablespoon, and decrease the baking soda slightly by indenting your finger into these ingredients while leveling the measuring spoon.

1. Thoroughly grease an 8x8-inch pan with pan spray, butter or margarine.

2. Mix together the brown sugar, canola oil, yogurt, vanilla, flour, baking powder and spices on medium high speed until very smooth.

3. Mix the oats and fruit into the creamy mixture at low speed and then mix all the ingredients together until they are thoroughly incorporated.

4. Spread the batter evenly into the prepared pan and then bake for 25-35 minutes or until an inserted knife or toothpick comes out clean.

5. Allow the steam to evaporate for a few minutes before covering the pan with plastic wrap or slicing into individual bars. Individual bars can be wrapped in plastic wrap and stay fresh for at least 3 days. Store excess in the freezer, once wrapped and placed into a freezer-safe bag.

Beauty in the Bean

Chocolate often described as *"sensational, ambrosial, sensual, luscious, heavenly, etc.,"* originates from the bitter tasting Cacao (pronounced Kakăw') Bean, commonly referred to as the Cocoa Bean. Once the beans are fermented, roasted and processed, they then become Chocolate, a favorite flavor and treat for many, as it is available most everywhere, in various forms and flavors these days. Yet it was only a few centuries ago when chocolate was considered a fine treasure and used as a form of money. Although no longer used as money for trade, there are varieties of chocolates that are indeed quite valuable to maintaining a healthy body and weight. You see Dark Chocolates (semi-sweet, bittersweet and unsweetened) are like a treasure to our bodies when eaten in small amounts, as they are bursting with antioxidants and vitamins. On the other hand, milk chocolate contains less natural cocoa and a lot more fat and sugar, thus not very beneficial and much more fattening than the darker varieties. Furthermore, when you take into consideration that the cost of candy is constantly rising as the price of sugar increases, it is recommended to make your own chocolate candies and treats, with healthful ingredients added for good measure, at a much lower cost to both the body as well as your wallet.

Happystacks

Many may be familiar with this recipe by its more common name "Haystacks." As a kid I always called them Happystacks; probably because the awesome flavor always made me feel so good. The best part about this recipe is that the ingredients can be altered meet the personal preferences for flavor. For instance, if your kids are allergic to nuts, then don't add any, add extra fruits instead.

✧

Serving size: 3-4 per person, depending on age

---

1 cup (6 ounces) semi-sweet chocolate chips

1-2 teaspoons butter

½ cup dark or golden raisins or a variety of chopped dried fruits

½ cup chopped nuts (optional)

2 cups chow mein noodles (amount can be adjusted per personal preference)

2 tablespoons shredded unsweetened coconut (optional)

1. Using a microwave-safe bowl, heat the chocolate chips and butter for about a minute in the microwave. Remove the bowl and then stir in the chocolate chips until thoroughly melted and smooth. Depending on the strength of your microwave oven, the chips may need a few more seconds in the microwave to melt completely.

2. Mix the remaining choice of ingredients into the melted chocolate until all ingredients are thoroughly coated.

3. Using a medium-sized spoon, drop individual mounds of the mixture onto a piece of waxed paper.

4. Refrigerate the candies for about an hour or until firm.

5. Store leftovers in a cool spot or in the refrigerator in a lined can with a lid, a plastic container with a tight fitting lid or wrapped in plastic wrap.

Banana Pops

These frozen treats are often described as "to die for." And no wonder! They are much healthier than ice cream and some of the prepackaged, frozen popsicles. So, how could you resist indulging your family with such a divine, edible pleasure? They're easy to prepare, so why not get the kids to help make them too; and relish in their company while they are still young, for they do grow up much too fast.

✧

Serves 4-6
(Large banana halves are the perfect size for the younger kids who have yet to enter school.)

4-6 popsicle or kabob skewer sticks

4 large, firm bananas (for best flavor buy bananas without any brown spots.)

1 teaspoon butter

1- 1¼ cups semi-sweet chocolate chips or 8 ounce dark chocolate bar, broken into small pieces

1. Without peeling the bananas, slice a ¼ inch or less from the bottom of each banana (slice in half, crosswise for younger children), and then very carefully insert the skewer or popsicle stick into the bottom center of each banana and gently push it halfway up the banana's length. (You do not want the stick to puncture through the side of the fruit.)

2. Wrap each banana in waxed paper or plastic wrap, place them onto a baking pan or cookie sheet, and freeze for one hour.

3. Approximately 10-15 minutes before removing the bananas from the freezer, line a baking pan or cookie sheet with waxed paper.

4. Melt the chocolate and butter in a double boiler (or casserole dish) above simmering water. Once the chocolate begins to melt, stir it constantly with a rubber spatula to prevent possible burning.

5. Remove the bananas from the freezer, and then carefully peel the skin off of each.

6. Turn the heat off under the pan, but do not yet discard the hot water or remove the bowl filled with melted chocolate from on top of the hot water.

7. Working quickly, dip each banana into the melted chocolate to coat. Holding the banana over the pan/bowl, you may wish to spoon and smooth some of the creamy chocolate over the fruit to ensure that it is completely coated and to prevent any chocolate droplets from escaping onto your stovetop. (If the melted chocolate begins to get too thick from the cold bananas, you will need to reheat and stir it again over simmering water.)

8. Place each Banana Pop onto the prepared pan, and then allow the chocolate to set and firm for about 20 minutes. If the air is warm or hot in your kitchen, allow the chocolate to set and firm in the refrigerator.

9. Once the chocolate is firm, wrap each Banana Pop in waxed paper, and then freeze them for at least 30 minutes before eating. These luscious treats will stay fresh for up to one week in the freezer.

✧ ✧ ✧

✐ VARIATION ✐

✧ Roll or sprinkle the banana pops in finely chopped nuts or colorful sprinkles before the chocolate cools and sets.

Chocolate Covered Treats

In consideration that most kids love chocolate and that the cost of an average chocolate candy bar is almost $1, why not make your own chocolate bars instead for about a quarter of the price, if not less. Just check out these easily prepared variations and enjoy the diversity of flavors. Although these recipes are terrifically easy and produce a succulent flavor, know that the best part about them is that they cost much less than candy bars do, and provide superb bodily benefits in comparison. Remember, dark chocolate, such as semi sweet chocolate, is advantageous for our bodies when offered in small amounts.

✧

CHOCOLATE COVERED FRUITS

Makes 6-8 servings

1 cup (6 ounces) semi-sweet chocolate chips or dark chocolate bar broken into small pieces

1 teaspoon butter

¾-1 cup fresh berries, cherries or large dried fruits, (apricots, pineapple, guava, papaya, mango, prunes, figs, dates, etc.)

1. Melt the chocolate and butter together in a microwave-safe bowl until smooth and creamy, about 1 minute. Stir the chocolate and butter together and if some lumps remain, reheat the mixture for a few more seconds.

2. While the chocolate is melting, line a large plate or baking pan with waxed paper.

3. Using your fingers or a toothpick dip the fresh or dried fruit into the melted chocolate (definitely use toothpicks to dip small berries or cherry halves into the chocolate with) and then set each to cool on a piece of waxed paper until firm.

4. Store chocolate covered fruit in the refrigerator, until serving to prevent the chocolate from softening too much.

✧ ✧ ✧

⌒VARIATION⌒

✧ To make **Chocolate Covered Pretzels**, substitute pretzel stick for the fruit, and dip the sticks into the melted chocolate and proceed accordingly. For an extra special treat, roll the chocolate-coated pretzel into chopped nuts or sprinkle immediately after dipping it.

✧

CHOCOLATE BARS

Serves 6-8

1 cup (6 ounces) semi-sweet chocolate chips or dark chocolate bar broken into small pieces

1 teaspoon butter

¾-1 cup nuts, Rice Crispies or small dried fruits (raisins)

1. Melt the chocolate and butter together in a microwave-safe bowl until smooth and creamy, about 1 minute. Stir the chocolate and butter together and if some lumps remain, reheat the mixture for a few more seconds.

2. While the chocolate is melting, line a 8x8 or 9x9 inch pan with waxed paper.

3. Sprinkle the nuts, cereal or dried fruits evenly over the waxed paper.

4. Pour the chocolate on top the ingredient of choice, and then using a rubber spatula, spread the chocolate around to completely coat the ingredient. Allow this mixture to harden until solid in the refrigerator, and then break it into 6-8 pieces and serve accordingly. Wrap excess pieces in plastic wrap and store in the refrigerator for up to 1 week.

✧ ✧ ✧

⌒VARIATION⌒

✧ For a change, use a tropical combination of flavors, such as ¼ cup chopped macadamia nuts, ⅓ cup chopped dried pineapple and about a tablespoon of tropical dried fruit bits.

Chocolaty Fruit Crèmes

Even Willy Wonka would approve of this recipe. For all kids, young and old, these incredibly superb, creamy little treats can be prepared with or without the chocolate coating. Ah, but once you smear, dip or drizzle each with the smooth comforting essence of chocolate bliss — they become fabulously irresistible.

✧

Small container of previously mixed fruit or vanilla yogurt

1-2 firm bananas

½ cup semi-sweet chocolate chips

1. Line a cookie sheet or baking pan with waxed paper.

2. Peel and slice the bananas into ½-inch slices.

3. Open the yogurt container, pour off any excess liquid and stir it a few times.

4. Using a toothpick or a fork, dip each banana slice into the yogurt to coat and then place each onto the prepared pan. Continue this dipping procedure until all banana slices are coated and then cover the pan with tin foil and freeze them for about 20-25 minutes or until serving. (these treats taste great just as they are once frozen.)

5. Just before removing the coated banana chips from the freezer, place the chocolate chips in a small bowl and then heat them for 40-50 seconds in the microwave or until the chips begin to melt. Using a rubber spatula stir the chips until thoroughly melted and smooth.

6. Using a fork or a toothpick, gently to lift each banana slice and dip it into the melted chocolate, and then place each back onto the waxed paper lined pan. Or, you may find it easier to scoop the chocolate with a small spoon, and then drizzle a small amount over each banana coated slice.

7. Allow the chocolate to set and cool and then place the slices into a freezer-safe baggie or thick plastic container with a tight fitting lid. Preferably separate the slices into rows, and place a piece of waxed paper in-between the layers. These freeze well for up to 5 days, if they last that long.

8. To serve, place the slices in a cool bowl and enjoy!

Stocking Up for Health

$$\mathcal{C} \smallsmile \diamondsuit \smallsmile \mathcal{O}$$

I t is common knowledge that the cost of food is constantly on the rise. However, do not allow this fact to prevent you from making better food decisions for your family. In fact, you can actually save money while food shopping; that is if you do so wisely. You see all you need to do is make a few moderate changes in everyday favored delights for those more healthful and stock up on various foods for health and flavor when these choices are fresh and/or available at a lower cost.

Fruits and vegetables are bountiful during late spring, summer and early autumn months. How could you resist purchasing these products in bulk? Commonly the prices for such healthful choices are much lower at flea markets, farmer markets and at local fruit stands than they are during the chilly months of winter. Besides, who could resist the magnificent flavors and sensual aromas elicited from a fresh harvest, especially when available in bulk at reasonable prices? Even when freshly frozen, the scent of summer remains within in the fruit all winter long. Plus, fresh frozen fruits make terrific snacks, and can be used in numerous foods, including adding a fruity flavor to a simple bottle of water. You know that fresh frozen veggies help make life easier when preparing meals in a jiffy. Yet, why would you waste your hard earned funds buying the prepackaged varieties when you can purchase more in bulk and freeze them yourself? Or, if space allows, you can grow some of your own fruits and veggies, and store the excess in the freezer for use at another time. In fact, all you need is a little patch of grass or dirt, which can be planted and transformed into a small garden of edible delight.

If you live in what has been termed a "Produce Desert" (*Denver Post*, 2010) whereby access to fresh fruits and veggies is limited within your neighborhood, do not give in to your residential circumstances. With motivation and a small amount of effort you can still gain access to these highly tasty and beneficial foods. For instance, you could start a weekly carpool with neighbors, and then drive to the farmer's markets, larger grocery stores or fruit stands. Or, you could even start your own local produce delivery service in your neighborhood. There are many farmers and produce distributors that would sell you fresh produce at wholesale prices to be resold to those in your neighborhood, at a discounted price. Also, neighborhood garden organizations are springing up throughout the US. These organizations help people to plant produce and herbal seeds in parks, along streets and even in abandoned lots. The seeds are tended to and cared for by volunteers (you and your children), who also take home some of the fragrant goodness of their efforts—once harvested. By the way, having your kids involved in such community efforts, will not only provide freshly grown produce, but will get your kids involved in a fun physical activity, as well as instilling pride in their community.

Another way to save is to stock up on cooking/baking ingredients and supplies during holiday sales. Oh my, for years to date, I personally have stocked up on butters, cooking oils, spices, herbs, flours, sugars, nuts and dark chocolates during the winter holidays. In fact, I try to save at least $5 per week per year, just for this purpose. Whenever, any of these ingredients go on sale, I stock up on them to use throughout the months ahead. I mean why spend over $3 on a 5-pound bag of flour, when you can get two of the same bags for $4 during the holidays. Butter and cooking oils are ridiculously expensive during the year, but during a few holidays their prices are significantly lower; so I stock up on and refrigerate them for use another time. I also stock up on dried fruits when on sale. They may get a bit hard after a few months, but it is always best to soak them in hot water before adding to various recipes anyway. Nuts are fabulous treats and most are also placed on sale around the holidays, and can be used later in the year. Baking and cooking pans commonly go on sale during special holidays (Christmas and Easter) too, thus a perfect time to buy pans that will be used for many years; before they need to be replaced. Sure dairy products will expire, but always pick the containers with the latest expiration date, so that they won't go to waste. Also know that bulk warehouses are a super place to stock up on large containers of cooking oils, whole grain cereals, dairy products, spices, nuts, plastic wrap, baggies and paper goods.

Stocking up on produce and ingredients, not only saves money, it helps you to make healthier choices when feeding your family. Just imagine the heavenly fragrance and smiles elicited when serving a hot, homemade berry gobbler during a winter storm, or how about a cherry pie on New Years Day. Serving fresh frozen peas, grown naturally in your area, is much tastier than those stored in a can with excess liquid and salts added to preserve the peas and maximize the weight. Thus stock the freezer, pantry and cabinets and enjoy the palatable warmth of a fresh harvest all year long.

Here are a few experiential tips on stocking up for health.

✦

🧑‍🍳HINTS

🍒 Use freezer-safe bags or thick, sturdy plastic containers for storing various fresh foods in the freezer. If using freezer-safe bags, make sure that you squeeze out all excess air once filled and before sealing each bag. Additionally, freezer-safe bags can be reused, as long as they don't have any holes. Simply invert the bag once empty and thoroughly clean and then dry each or allow them to dry in the open air. Invert them once again, and fill accordingly!

🍒 Large, plastic storage containers commonly go on sale during annual holidays, as well as just before the kids go back to school after summer's break. These containers are perfect for storing bags of flours and sugars in. For convenience purposes, it is suggested to label each bag/container with a permanent marker or piece of tape listing the contents.

FRUITS

Peaches, plums, apricots, and nectarines: Wash and blanch the fruit in boiling water for 3-5 minutes. Remove from the water, drain, peel, pit, and slice in half or into thinner slices, and then freeze along with any excess juices.

Cherries: Wash, drain, pit, and freeze

Berries: Wash, drain and freeze. Of course a combination of diverse berries (blueberries, raspberries and blackberries) can be frozen together.

HINT: *Because strawberries get mushy when frozen, they do not do not freeze well; unless used when preparing smoothies or a sweet sauce used for toppings.*

Grapes: Wash, drain, and freeze.

Cranberries: Wash, drain and freeze.

Bananas: You will not need to freeze bananas in a freezer-safe bag, but freeze them while still greenish for maximum flavor. The skin will brown in the freezer, but the banana will stay stiff and fresh.

Pomegranates: Remove the seeds from the membranes, and place into a freezer-safe baggie or plastic container and freeze.

Pineapples: Cut away the peel, core the center, slice into rings or chunks, and then freeze with excess juices.

Citrus Fruits: These do not freeze well, so avoid freezing these healthful delights unless peeled, segmented, and mixed with other ingredients.

Papayas, Mangos and Guava: Although these fruits can be frozen up to a month, once sliced or scooped away from the rind, they can get mushy once frozen. Therefore, it is suggested to only freeze them for use in smoothies or as a flavorful addition when roasting various meats, fish or poultry.

Melons: Honeydew, cantaloupe, Crenshaw and watermelon can be sliced or scooped away from it's skin and then placed into a freezer-safe baggie or container with a couple tablespoons of water added to help maintain moisture. Frozen melons are splendid to use in Smoothies or Slushies.

Kiwi: Peel and eat these fresh for maximum flavor, for these colorful delights will get too mushy in the freezer to palatably enjoy.

✧

VEGETABLES

Asparagus, broccoli, cauliflower, green/wax beans, carrots, and peppers: Cut into 2-3 inch pieces, wash, blanch, cool, and freeze.

Peas: These can be washed and frozen in their pods or removed from the pods and frozen accordingly.

Brussels Sprouts: Trim off the bottoms and remove the dirty leaves away from the outer layer, and then blanch, cool, drain and freeze.

Spinach: Wash well, and then place them into a sieve and then rinse the spinach under cold water once again to remove any lingering dirt particles. Once the leaves are clean, bring a pot of water to a full boil. To blanch or steam, place the filled sieve into or above the boiling water until the leaves are dark green. Once the leaves are dark green, remove the sieve from the heat and thoroughly drain any excess liquid above the pot or over a sink and then gently pat the leaves dry

HINTS

- ❧ Wash, chop and blanch (immerse food in boiling water for a few minutes) or steam the veggies for 1-2 minutes, and then rinse them quickly under very cold-icy water to ensure that they maintain their shape and bright color. Thoroughly drain any excess liquid by patting the veggies dry with a paper towel before freezing.

- ❧ Use freezer-safe bags for then it is easier to remove the desire amount, without chiseling into the remaining frozen vegetable.

with a paper towel. Allow the leaves to cool and then chop or finely mince the leaves and then freeze accordingly.

Corn: Remove the husk, wash, blanch, cool, drain, and then scrape the kernels off of the stalk and into container and freeze. For use as cream corn, after draining, cut into about ½ the depth of the kernels and scrape with a knife into freezer bag. Then with the back of the knife, scrape the remaining the kernels into same freezer-safe bag and freeze.

Zucchini, eggplant and squash: Wash, cut into ½-1 inch sections, blanch, cool, drain, and freeze accordingly. (For Pumpkins, Acorns, Winter Squash, etc. remove the seeds before blanching, chopping and freezing.)

HINT

🍇 The above fruits and vegetables will stay well in a freezer for 7- 9 months or until the climate begins to warm away the winter chill, allowing the cornucopia of blooms to grow once again.

✧

DRY INGREDIENTS

Flours: Diverse flours commonly go on sale during various annual holidays. Therefore it is best to purchase several bags at a time and then store these bags in a dry, cool spot. Preferably, place the individual bags in thick, sturdy plastic containers with tight fitting lids to prevent rodents or bugs from entering the bags.

White Sugar: Because the price of sugar is consistently on the rise, definitely stock up on it when placed on sale. Sugar, including confection or icing sugar, is also best stored in a cool, dry space and/or in large plastic containers. Additionally, search for the best prices before purchasing and storing. For instance one grocery store may have a sale price for two, 5-pound bags at $5, while the grocery store 2 blocks away may set the price for two, 5-pound bags at $4 for the same product.

Brown Sugar: The cost of dark brown sugar also is on the rise, thus when it is placed sale purchase several bags, and then store them first in larger plastic bags, and then in a large plastic container, if available. Also, add a couple small pieces of orange peel into the larger bag or container to help prevent it from getting hard. Because brown sugar is made from molasses added to white sugar, for best flavor only purchase the darker varieties and those in which you cannot see any white sugar granules, whatsoever.

Spices, Jarred Herbs and Extracts: Although bulk suppliers usually have the best prices for these healthful and stupendous flavor enhancers, stock up and save when placed on sale. Spices and herbs are commonly healthful and really can turn a plain everyday dish into one filled with a remarkable refreshing flavor. Also, pure flavoring extracts (i.e. vanilla, almond, lemon etc.), definitely add a distinctive, awesome flavors to the products in which they are added. Because you only wish to use those varieties that are pure, rather than those artificially flavored with chemicals, purchase the largest containers when on sale and know that they will not be wasted, but used often.

Dried Fruits and Nuts: Best purchased in bulk when on sale, and then stored in their packaging. Once opened, store the excess in a baggie or plastic container. Additionally, if nut trees grown in your neighborhood, you can save lots of money on these healthy treats by getting you kids to actively meander around the neighborhood gathering them in bags to be shelled and used at another time.

Butter, Margarine and Canola-based Butter Spreads: Because these ingredients are commonly used daily in and on various foods, absolutely stock up on them during sales. As long as they are refrigerated or placed in the freezer, they will stay fresh for 8-12 months.

Chocolate: Best purchased when on sale, whether you choice is semi-sweet chocolate chips, or bars of dark chocolate. Keep in mind that around various holidays a grand assortment of chocolates, especially semi-sweet chocolate chips, go on sale! So stock up several bags and bars at a time, for then you will have them available for use during the months ahead. It is best to store dark chocolate in a cool, dark spot, as refrigerating or freezing it for long periods of time may cause discoloration.

HINT

❦ Overall the more you buy when these ingredients are on sale, the more you save and have rapidly available in the long run.

In summary, it doesn't matter if you live in a mansion, row house, or far out in a rural community, your children will still depend on you to make the best decisions for them that you are able to. Being a parent is the most difficult job you will ever take on, and the only job that lasts a lifetime. You won't get a paycheck, but when perform your daily duties with a full heart, enthusiasm, and with the best of intentions, you do get reimbursed with the priceless offering of hugs, kisses and smiles between the tears.

As your kids get older, they will often seek your advice, whether this is how to change a diaper, temper your grandbaby's sniffles, how to pick the most appropriate outfit for an interview, or even how to make a great meal.

As previously said, you are your children's role model, so make the best choices for your kids that you can. Even when they may challenge your choices, know that you have made them as an offering of your love and that they will adjust with consistency, as they have no other choice. Lastly, always remember that the lessons, guidance, rules and flavors that you provide for your babes will affect their lives, health and memories for years and generations to come. So love them a little bit more, feed them less.

Substitutions and Equivalents

One of the most important sections of any recipe book is the Substitution section. How many times have you grabbed for an ingredient halfway through mixing a recipe and you are out of it or do not have it? This has happened to me more times then I can count. The following is a list of substitutions and measuring equivalents that can be used in the recipes found among the previous pages; unless specified otherwise.

✧

When the Recipe Calls for	You can use:
1 cup flour	¾ cup plus 2 tablespoons whole wheat flour, or for wheat less product use ¾ cup plus 2 tablespoons Buckwheat flour mixed with 2 tablespoons quinoa flour
1 cup sugar	1 cup of a sugar substitute such as Twin or Stevia. When measuring, measure the substitute to just below the required measuring cup line
1-pound box of powdered sugar	Equivalent to 3½ - 3¾ cups of powdered sugar
1 tablespoon of cornstarch	2 tablespoons flour when used for thickening purposes
1 teaspoon of baking powder	½ teaspoon cream of tarter and ¼ teaspoon baking soda, for leavening purposes

When the Recipe Calls for	You can use:
2½ tablespoons tapioca	only use minute tapioca in these recipes. This is equivalent to 5 tablespoon pearl tapioca soaked in water or 2½ tablespoon flour
½ cup of margarine or butter	½ cup is equivalent to 1 stick or a ¼-pound of butter or margarine. Unless specified otherwise they can be used in place of the other.
½ cup melted margarine	Unless specified otherwise, ¼ cup of canola oil and ¼ cup melted margarine can be used instead of ½ cup melted margarine. This does not always apply to melted butter.
1 cup canola oil	1 cup of sunflower or safflower oil. Do not use corn oil, any other kind of vegetable oil, olive oil or peanut oil.
1 cup milk	½ cup evaporated milk mixed with ½ cup water
1 cup buttermilk	1 tablespoon lemon juice or vinegar, and enough milk to fill a cup. Also buttermilk can be substituted with a cup of plain yogurt in many recipes.
1 cup sour cream	1 cup plain yogurt, or 1 tablespoon lemon juice mixed enough evaporated milk to fill a cup
Eggs	Equivalent amount of liquid egg substitute, check container for equal amount. 1 extra-large egg is equivalent to 2 small eggs

When the Recipe Calls for	You can use:
1 teaspoon of lemon zest	Zest is the grated rind of the lemon. 1 lemon rind will grate to 1 teaspoon. If you do not have fresh lemons available, ½ teaspoon of lemon extract is also equivalent to 1 teaspoon of lemon zest. Also when fully squeezed, 1 lemon will give you just shy of 2 tablespoons of juice.
1 teaspoon or more of vanilla	Only use pure vanilla extract or 1 teaspoon of Kahlúa® Liqueur.
1 square unsweetened chocolate	3 tablespoons of cocoa mixed with 1 tablespoon butter
6 cups of peeled and sliced apples	6 large apples
6 cups peeled and sliced peaches	9-10 large peaches or 4 cans of sliced peaches drained of juice or water
1 cup shredded cheese	4-5 ounces of grated cheese. But remember cheese is much less expensive when purchased in block and then grated for use.
1 cup chopped walnuts, almonds and pecans	Walnuts, almonds and pecans can be used interchangeably. 1 cup chopped pecans is equivalent to about 5 ounces, about 6 ounces for both walnuts and almonds.

Index

❦

Italics = Name of Recipe

About the Author

Randi Levin was raised in Philadelphia, and introduced to the preparation of good food in her grandmothers' kitchens long before she entered school. While in high school she began acquiring the skills necessary for helping others at the Philadelphia Child Guidance Clinic, a facility she would return to for training and employment. Equipped with a passion, dedication and a natural instinct for helping others, she went on to become highly educated and trained as a teacher and mental health professional. Many years were occupied helping children and families overcome obstacles related to learning disabilities, behavioral disorders, eating disorders, emotional traumas or just common childhood confusions related to growing up healthy and wise.

In the early 1990's, residing in the mountains of Colorado, Randi's life and career changed in a moment due to a medical condition. Yet, she never gave in; instead she found another way to help others through the goodness of homemade food and her cookbooks, *Baking at High Altitude* and *Sharing Mountain Recipes*.

Today she is an internationally awarded culinary author, who believes that knowledge and good food should be shared; and that helping others is a gift. Because, her passion for helping remains strong, she often reflects on the lessons students and clients taught her to help guide her eternal path to help them and their parents make the best choices that they can for health, well being and life.